1600 - 1947
ANGLO-INDIAN LEGACY

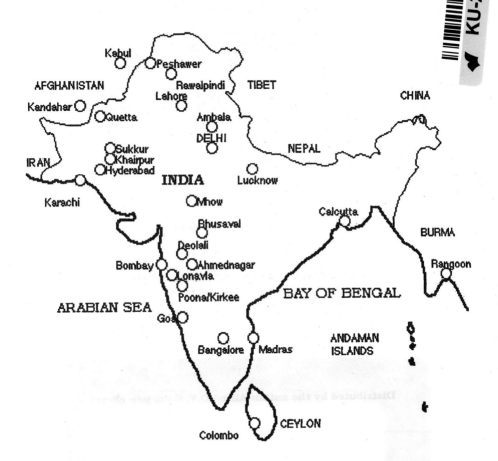

A BRIEF GUIDE TO BRITISH RAJ INDIA HISTORY, NATIONALITY, EDUCATION, RAILWAYS & IRRIGATION.

By Alfred D.F. (George) Gabb, C.Eng., M.I.C.E.
Chartered Civil Engineer

REVISED 2ND EDITION

First published 1998
Revised 2nd Edition 2000

ISBN 0 948333 89 8

British Libraries Cataloguing-in-Publication Data
Alfred D.F. (George) Gabb 2000
1600-1947 Anglo-Indian Legacy:
A Brief Guide to British Raj India History,
Nationality, Education, Railways & Irrigation

CONTENTS

If I should die, think only this of me:
That there's some corner of a foreign field
That is forever England
('The Soldier' by Rupert Brooke 1887-1915)

MAPS & ILLUSTRATIONS

ACKNOWLEDGEMENTS

Hundreds of talented authors have written many and varied books about India. I am grateful to those whose books I have read, and where of use to my thesis I have tried to acknowledge them generally in the text. They are all listed in my Selected Bibliography, together with other worthwhile books I would have liked to have read also. I would especially like to acknowledge Hazel Innes Craig for 'The Old School Toppee' © 1996, the Indian Government for the 'Council for the Indian School Certificate Examinations, School Lists' © 1993 and the Telegraph Group Ltd, London © 1995, 1996 and 1997 for the Daily and Sunday Telegraph newspaper articles on India and 'The British Empire' © 1997.

I would like to thank the Rector of St Joseph's Boys High School, Bangalore for permission to reproduce the school magazine cover photo, the Principal of Barnes School, Deolali for permission to reproduce the school greetings card picture of the school painted by Fenton Bailey in 1945, and Hunting Technical Services Ltd of Hertfordshire for permission to reproduce the aerial photograph of Mohenjo Daro.

I would like to thank my elder sister Lawna Allen (nèe Gabb), my elder brother Patrick Gabb and my younger sister Janet Eden (nèe Gabb), who like me were brought up in India, for their encouragement and support. I would particularly like to thank my sister Lawna Allen for painstakingly reading, and re-reading my efforts, making corrections and otherwise making useful comment.

Not least I would like to thank my long suffering wife Angela for her patience and forbearance, for her check of part of the draft and for acting as a sounding board!

Revised 2nd Edition AD 2000

I would like to thank my readers for their kind letters, especially those who once lived and worked in British *Raj* India, and now live in Britain, Australia, New Zealand, Canada, U.S.A., South Africa, and elsewhere, and also those that stayed behind in the post-*Raj* countries of India, Pakistan and Bangladesh. Their expressions of appreciation, and kindness in sharing their knowledge, family connections and experiences in the subcontinent are very much appreciated. It is also good to hear from the post-*Raj* generations too. I should also like to thank B.A.C.S.A. (*Chowkidar*), the *Indiaman Magazine*, *Family Tree Magazine*, Indian Army Association, Society of Genealogists, London, the *U.K. Josephites Journal* and the Irish Family History Society for their generous reviews of the first edition, short 'clips' from which appear on the back cover. Publicity from School and general India associations is also greatly appreciated. I have taken the opportunity to revise and update the book, and add another 150 or so *Anglo-Indian* schools.

A.D.F.G.
April 2000

INTRODUCTION

It seems particularly poignant that this book should be written in 1997, exactly 50 years after India was granted independence from the British *Raj* on 15th August 1947. That was the year of the great exodus from India of most of the *Europeans* and *Anglo-Indians* resident there, the descendents of nearly 350 years of British service, or business. Apart from a few, their services were no longer required, as the new nations of India and Pakistan strove at first to find their own 'place in the sun'. I left India that year also, bound for Britain and higher education, to become a Civil Engineer. I was born in Poona (*Pune*) in India in 1930. I was educated in St.Joseph's College, Bangalore and Barnes High School, Deolali (*Devlali*). I did not return to the sub-continent until 1961, when I was engaged for 5 years as a Resident Consulting Engineer with the Pakistan Government on the Lower Indus Project Report, an investigation into the irrigation and land drainage development of the great river barrage systems of the Sind, which spawned perhaps the largest civil engineering development works of their kind in the world. As a former child of the *Raj* I took great pride in participating in this great scheme, and in being able to contribute with my first hand knowledge of the Indian sub-continent. I regrettably did not return again until 1995, probably the last time I shall see this wonderful country.

To the best of my knowledge all my ancestors went to India from Ireland and England in the 19th century. They served in the Honourable East India Company Army (E.I.C.), the British Army, the Royal Ordnance, the Medical Services and the Indian Railways. Of those I am certain about one of my paternal great grandfathers was a Hospital Steward in 1853 in Poona attached to the 1st Bombay (*European*) Fusilliers of the E.I.C., the first E.I.C. Regiment to be formed, which in 1861 became the Royal Bombay Fusiliers. Later he became an Apothecary with the Medical Establishment in Bombay (*Mumbai*). He was at the Indian Mutiny of 1857. One of my maternal great grandfathers enlisted as a Private in the 3rd Dragoon Guards in Cork, in Ireland in 1865, before leaving for India, and was later transferred to the 18th Hussars whilst with General Napier in Ethiopia in 1868. Later still he became a Gunner in the Royal Horse Artillery, and was with General Roberts and Burrows in Afghanistan from 1878 to 1880. He took his discharge after 23 years in Kirkee (*Khadki*), near Poona, where I was brought up. His son, my maternal grandfather was a Foreman Engineer from 1885 in the Royal Ordnance Factory in Kirkee, as was his son after him. His daughter, my mother, served in the Women's Voluntary Service (WVS) during World War 2, 1939 - 1945 in Kirkee, and sadly suffered an early death in India. My other paternal great grandfather and his son went to India from London in England to serve in the Great Indian Peninsula Railway in 1891 and 1892 respectively. The former was Foreman

Boilersmith in the Railway Workshops at Byculla in Bombay, and the latter was Foreman Engineering Fitter in the Engineering Workshops at Bhusaval, before both suffered early deaths, the latter from smallpox. The latter's son, my late father, was born in Bhusaval.

My father was educated at the prestigious La Martinère College, Lucknow, and was a Sergeant in the 2nd Battalion Dorset Regiment in Mesopotamia during the Great War 1914-1918. Later he was in commerce in Bombay before joining the Royal Ordnance Ammunition Factory in Kirkee, as a Foreman Engineer in 1926. Subsequently he became the Superintendent Storekeeper. During World War 2, 1939 - 1945, he was a Frontiersman in the Voluntary Reserve. My sister served as a Subaltern in the Women's Auxiliary Corps, India (WAC(I)) during World War 2 in Lahore. Her husband was a Flying Officer from London in the Royal Air Force in India. Three of my uncles were senior officers in the Royal Engineers in India. One was a Power Station Engineer at Quetta during the 1935 earthquake and later back home the Garrison Engineer of Salisbury. The others were based in Quetta, Poona and Delhi. Another uncle was a British Army Officer in Dehra Dun, and later Manager of a cotton mill in Bombay. A further uncle was Superintendent of the Royal Ordnance Factory at Kirkee and a Factory Consultant at Jubbulpore post-*Raj* for a while. Others included a senior Police Inspector and a commercial Manager in Bombay.

When on my retirement I came to researching the genealogy and history of my family, I realised how little I really knew of the history and achievements of the British in India over 350 years, since Queen Elizabeth I had granted a Royal Charter to the East India Company in 1600. I seemed to have learnt more in school about Shivaji the Great, the dashing *Maratha* Chieftain from Poona, than I had of Lord Robert Clive, the remarkable British General, a founder of the great British Indian Empire, or indeed of the infamous Indian Mutiny of 1857. I was ignorant of the nationalities of major players in British *Raj* history, and in particular unclear of the background of the mixed blood *Anglo-Indians*, that much maligned race during the last 100 years of the *Raj*, who outnumbered the discriminatory *European* ruling class who treated them as second class citizens. The words *European* and *Anglo-Indian* have been high-lighted throughout in italics in the text for clarity, as their difference became a very sensitive matter during the *Raj*. Thankfully it has not perpetuated since Indian Independence, for the majority of *Anglo-Indians* who moved to western and other Commonwealth countries, such as Britain, U.S.A., Canada, Australia, New Zealand and South Africa, have become equal and successful citizens in society there. My detail exposè of the *Anglo-Indian* and *Domiciled European* community treatment during the *Raj* is also in no way meant to be offensive or derogatory, but the reality as I knew it, and research has revealed. Rather it will show that in the non-racial and politically correct Britain of today, the British 'country born' of India, the *Anglo-Indians*, and even the *Domiciled Europeans*, are owed by the British nation both a debt of gratitude, for the great success of the *Raj*, and an apology for their treatment during the *Raj*.

Having read many of the thousands of books written about India in my family history research, I decided to write a *resumè* of the fascinating social, civil and military legacy of the British *Raj*, including some of the spectacular achievements of the Engineers, especially in Irrigation, Roads and Railways, arms of the Civil Engineering industry, which have occupied a large part of my professional career in the sub-continent, and elsewhere in the Commonwealth and Britain in the last fifty years.

I also found I knew little of the background of the day and boarding schools I attended all my youth in India. I was to discover there were hundreds of good quality *Anglo-Indian* schools in addition to my own, attended probably by more *European* and *Anglo-Indian* children than returned to England for this purpose. All told the breadth of British endeavour and achievement amounts to a remarkable *Anglo-Indian* Legacy.

It occurs to me that my background research titled '*Anglo-Indian Legacy - A Brief Guide to British Raj India History, Nationality, Education, Railways and Irrigation*' may well be of interest to my family, relatives, friends, and other family historians, ex-India hands and their children, and others interested in British Indian history. With apologies for 'Kilroy was here' references in the text!

Alfred D.F.(George) Gabb
York, England
15 August 1997.

I dedicate this book to
my late dear mother Eileen Mary Gabb (nèe Callaghan),
who died before her time in India;
my beloved late father David Edward Franklin Gabb
and also to
all former Anglo-Indians and Domiciled Europeans from British Raj India

PART 1

ANGLO-INDIANS

Forgotten Pioneers of an Empire

We've drunk to the Queen- God Bless her! -
We've drunk to our mother's land;
We've drunk to our English brother,
(But he does not understand);
We've drunk to the wide creation,
And the Cross swings low for the morn,
Last toast, and of obligation,
A health to the Native-born!

('*The Native-born*' by Rudyard Kipling 1894)

1. The Indian Conundrum -

THE REMARKABLE LAND known as India before 1947, spanned a whole subcontinent of Asia, extending from the Himalayan Mountains in the north, on the border with China, to the Indian ocean in the south, the mountains of Afghanistan in the west and the jungles of Burma in the east, nearly 2000 miles each way. The name 'India', said to be derived through the Greeks from the Persianised form of the Sanskrit word *sindhu* (river), preeminently the Indus, one of the longest rivers in the world, became familiar only after the British connection.[29]   Indeed the southern part of the great River Indus basin, where one of the most ancient cities in the world, namely Mohenjo-Daro (c 2500 B.C.), is located, is known as the Sind. Immediately prior to the British *Raj* the bulk of the land was under *Moghul* domination and was known as *Hindustan*.

The British Empire at its peak, just prior to Indian independence in 1947, and during the reign of King George VI (1936 - 1952), amounted to over 14 million square miles of territory, with a combined population of over 500 million people. That is about 120 times the area and 13 times the population of the United Kingdom at that time. British territories extended to all parts of the globe, from the deep tropics of Africa and the exotic orient to the wide plains of Canada and Australia. Its peoples varied from white-

1

skinned Christian *Europeans*, and brown-skinned *Muslim* Arabs and Indian *Hindus*, to yellow-skinned Chinese *Buddhists* and black-skinned pagan Africans and Australian aborigines.   It was *'the empire on which the sun never set'*, and covered about a quarter of the inhabited world. There was more British 'pink' than any other colour, on the map of the world, in every school atlas.   Of this, the British Indian Empire, acquired more by accident than by design, during the collapse of the *Moghul* Empire and ensuing chaos, and located 6,000 miles away from England (by sea), alone amounted to just over 1.5 million square miles, and equally significantly had a population of nearly 400 million people. That is, although only covering about a tenth of the area of the British Empire, it was populated by over three quarters of the people, or about 10 times the population of Britain.104 It was therefore all the more remarkable that this country of India was often said to have been ruled and administered, at the turn of the century, by only   about 1000 or so very well paid   *European* administrators; senior covenanted members of the Indian Civil Service, or I.C.S., the so-called 'heaven born' of Rudyard Kipling, the best known *Domiciled European* of them all, who was born in Bombay. They came from the top English public schools and the 'Oxbridge' universities, and the old East India Company inspired Haileybury College, in Hertfordshire, and were alleged to be the best paid civil servants in the world.18,63 These illustrious and remarkable Governors-General, Viceroys (see Appendix 1), Governors, Commissioners, Collectors and District Officers have been well documented, and publicised by numerous popular publications over the last 350 years of the British influence in India. However, relatively less publicity has been given to the lesser mortals, the *Domiciled Europeans*, and much maligned *Anglo-Indians*, described by some as 'poor whites', who ran the country so ably up until Indian Independence in 1947.

> *'According to Census returns of 1931 the population included 306,529 persons of European and allied races (including Armenians) viz. 155,555 British Subjects, 12,579 persons of other European races and 138,395 Anglo-Indians. Similar results for 1941 are not available. The description of an Anglo-Indian for Census purposes was a person whose father, grandfather or other progenitor in the male line was an European'.*
> 104

In addition, about 50 thousand *European* and *Anglo-Indian* military personnel maintained in the country played a magnificent part in both keeping the peace and protecting the frontiers of India. Much has been written of their successful and illustrious leaders, but rather less about the terrible loneliness and privation of the common soldier, the British other ranks (B.O.R.) and non-commissioned officers (N.C.O.), the 'cannon fodder' of early warfare, and treated as such, except as brought to the notice of the public by the entertaining prose and poetry of Rudyard Kipling.

The Honourable East India Company (E.I.C.) had its own army and navy. The military officers were all trained from 1809 to 1861, at the E.I.C. Military Seminary, at Addiscombe, near Croydon, in Surrey. The Engineers and Artillery also attended the Royal Military Academy at Woolwich in

London and the School of Military Engineering, Chatham, in Kent. Before the British Government assumed full military and civil power in India in 1858 all Civil Engineering work, apart from the Railways, was done by military Engineers of the armies of the E.I.C. This included roads, canals, water supply and public buildings. However subsequently with expansion of Civil Engineering works there was a shortage of Engineers for the Public Works Department, which was filled by the opening in 1871 of the Royal Indian Engineering College, Cooper's Hill, in Berkshire, (see also Appendix 3 and 4). The College later admitted students for the Indian Telegraph and Forestry Departments, before its final closure in 1903, by which time British public universities and colleges began to take on this education.[77]

Little has also been written in popular prose about the gigantic achievements of the Military and Civil Engineers in India, in developing the early communications, water supply and great irrigation works, which revolutionised government, business, travel and transport, and greatly raised living standards and transformed arid deserts into reliable food-productive land, thus reducing famine and poverty, in this vast and colourful country. Relatively less is also written about the success of the Government Public Works Department (P.W.D.), the Police, Forestry, Irrigation, Post and Telegraphs and Railways, and the colossal achievements of the Medical services (I.M.S. and I.M.D.), who by their dedication, controlled, and in some cases completely eradicated, the huge range of deadly endemic diseases, like typhoid, cholera, malaria, dysentery and smallpox, which tragically took so many children, and young and old adult *European* lives in the early days of the British *Raj*. This can be observed in cemeteries around the country, many of which sadly are falling into dereliction, but not without the sterling efforts to reverse this,and save their monumental inscriptions for posterity, by the '*British Association of Cemeteries in South Asia*' (B.A.C.S.A.), and their founder and Secretary Theon Wilkinson M.B.E., whose magazine the '*Chowkidar*' proudly relates their findings and success. Heat stroke, now known as heat exhaustion, was also a great taker of lives, in a country where the shade temperatures in large areas often flirted in summer with 120 degrees Fahrenheit and above, with humidity in the 90 percent during the wearisome *monsoon*, or otherwise in the area of rice paddies. I lost an uncle at the age of 15 years that way in Lonavla in 1917. Troops in battle suffered even greater privation especially in the early years of the *Raj*, as there was no treatment for tetanus arising from their wounds, and gangrene was commonplace. Many *Europeans* were 'driven to drink' to overcome their fears of prevalent disease and conditions of living. Venereal diseases (V.D.), such as syphilis and gonorrhoea were also rampant, especially amongst the other ranks of British troops, who were commonly forced, through circumstance, to use the services of native *bazaar* prostitutes and *nautch* girls for their pleasure and entertainment. In 1896 some fifty percent of the British Army were said to suffer from some form of venereal disease. The Army tried to reduce this by arranging for officially procured and medically monitored Indian women, to serve as official prostitutes, available to the troops at a ratio which rose to as high as one for every eleven soldiers. Unfortunately, although this proved successful for reducing infection, British Victorian society, especially back

Home in England, was so outraged at the effect on British social and religious morals, that the politicians were forced to ban it, and with terrible consequences. Disease and sickness continued to be the cause of high casualties, especially in the British and Indian Armies in Asia, even in more recent times. During the Second World War against the Japanese in Burma and Malaya from 1941 to 1945 malaria, beri beri and typhoid continued to take their toll.

By far the greater majority of the *Europeans* in India were from the British Isles, that is the present United Kingdom and Ireland, known collectively by the Indians as *'Angrezi log'* or English people, from *'Billayati'* or 'Blighty' (England), as it was known by the troops. It was even applied to *Europeans* from mainland Europe. In earlier years the name *'ferringhi'* was common also for foreigners. Other *Europeans* in India were Portuguese, French, Dutch, German and Scandinavian, although these date generally from the earlier years of trade and conquest, before total British domination after the Indian Mutiny in 1857.

2. Origin of the Species -

Both my parents and I were born in India; my father in Bhusaval and my mother and I in Poona (*Pune*), and we thought of ourselves as *Europeans*. The grandparents I knew were all white, but until such time as I am able to trace all branches of my family back to Europe, I would be unable to know for certain whether I carried the blood of 'Mother India' in my veins. Even then there is always fidelity in marriage to wonder about! Many *Europeans* started life in India in covenanted government posts, often remaining as such until retirement, and in so doing becoming domiciled in India. The 'country-born' descendants of the first generation *Europeans*, often secured uncovenanted Government posts as *Domiciled Europeans*, as they were to be later described. However, at first, before the time of the infamous Indian Mutiny in 1857, and during the reign of Queen Victoria of England (1837 - 1901), all *Europeans* who were born in India, or who spent most of their lives there, were known officially as *Anglo-Indians*. Persons of mixed *European* and Indian blood were known as 'Eurasian', 'East Indian', 'Indo-Briton', 'Topasses' [77], or even 'halfcaste'. After the British Government took direct control of the administration of the country from the E.I.C. in 1858, the latter began gradually to be known as *Anglo-Indian*, where the father of a child from the first liaison with an Indian woman was from Europe, and not just from Britain. It was however not officially recognised by the Government until the Census of 1911. Children of mixed blood, where the father of the first liaison was Indian, and the woman *European*, were known always as Indian. Persons of totally *European* blood, that is whose forbears both maternal and paternal were of *European* stock, and not just from Britain, but born in India, became known officially as *Domiciled Europeans*, to differentiate them from other 'country-born' *Anglo-Indians*, and from *Europeans* born in Great Britain. I can recollect *Anglo-Indians*, and even some *Domiciled Europeans*, including my father, referring to Indians as 'country cousins'. However there was constant confusion and not a little ill will about this differentiation, right up to the time of Indian Independence in 1947. This was not relieved by the tendency of the British Government to merge the *Domiciled European* and *Anglo-Indian* communities together, for their administrative convenience, when matters of race, nationality, education and employment were discussed, into the *'Anglo-Indian Community'*.[83] Voluntary Associations sometimes formed to further the interests of both communities generally, whilst maintaining their separate identities, as with the *'All-India Anglo-Indian and Domiciled European Association'*, combining only to further their common interests, that is until Indian Independence, when the *Anglo-Indians* remaining in India were encouraged to embrace Indian nationality and the term *Domiciled European* disappeared from official use, to be replaced by *European,* or Expatriate. A few *Domiciled Europeans* remained in India with a larger proportion of the *Anglo-Indians* after Independence, gradually 'fading away', with old age, as so well portrayed in Paul Scott's novel *'Staying On'.* [79]

At first there were few *European* women in India, as travel was difficult and hazardous and the country none too healthy for *Europeans.* In time, the Portuguese, Dutch and eventually the British East India Company in turn, drafted ship loads of unmarried *European* women to India, in their concern to satisfy the needs of their *European* employees and protect their morals. This however soon became very costly and supply was exceeded by demand. In the second half of the 17th century *European* men, the majority of whom were company soldiers, began to take to illicit sex with Indian women. In consequence the trading companies fell upon the solution to encourage legitimate marriage to the Indian natives, as a means to safely and respectably satisfy the needs of their employees, whilst also boosting the prospects for trade provided by their assimilation into the country. However, this did not turn out altogether as planned, as with the missionary zeal of the day, Indian girls had first to be converted to Christianity, which resulted in their complete ostracism from Indian society, where religion and caste play a leading role in Indian life. Also, their children at a stroke lost all prospects of employment, except within the *European* trading posts and in the army, whom they served very loyally and well. Many became mercenaries for the private armies of the Princely States. Some of the early off-spring of Portuguese mixed marriages, known as *'Luso-Indians'* and *'Ferringhis'*, are said to have become bandits and pirates, in the Arabian Sea and the Bay of Bengal. The latter term *Ferringhi* was also later used by the Indians in the 19th century to describe all *Europeans,* before settling upon *'Angrezi',* that is English, which they mostly were in the 20th century. The E.I.C. had issued an edict in 1687 which stated that

> *'The marriage of our soldiers to the native women of Fort St George is a matter of such consequence to posterity that we shall be content to encourage it with some expense, and have been thinking for the future to appoint a pagoda (eight or nine shillings in those days), to be paid to the mother of any child that shall hereafter be born of any such future marriage, upon the day the child is christened, if you think this small encouragement will increase the number of such marriages.'*

The creation of the *Anglo-Indian* Community was therefore officially encouraged by the Company, and resulted in a surge of respectable legitimate families, which have survived and multiplied to this day. The *Luso-Indians*, of Portuguese origin became mostly the *Goans* of the 20th century as intermarriage with the Indians continued. Originaly the child of a white father was called *'mestice'* and that of a white mother, of which there were a few, *'cestice'*.[91] Many moved to Calcutta *(Kolkata)*, but they were out-numbered by the *Anglo-Indians* whose indentity they commonly adopted. Many *Europeans* chose not to inter-marry with Indians, and as *Domiciled Europeans* provided sterling service to the Company and the Crown, in both civilian and military life. Many of these were brilliant servicemen, or civil administrators, and frequently called upon to be both.

3. Earlier White Migrants -

There had been earlier movements of white people into India hundreds of years before the appearance of the merchant adventures of western Europe. The original dark skinned peoples of India, or Dravidians, still evident in the south of India, were alleged to have been invaded in circa 1500 B.C. by fair skinned *Indo-European* Aryans, according to the hymns of the ancient *Hindu 'Rig Veda'*. They apparently used horse drawn chariots and worshipped gods similar to those of the then Greeks and Romans.[49] One theory is that the Aryans were responsible for the end of a then highly sophisticated Indus civilisation, evidenced from the ancient ruins of Harappa, in the Punjab, 100 miles south west of Lahore, Mohenjo-Daro ('mound of the dead') in the Sind, 250 miles north of Karachi, and many other smaller ruined towns and villages, said to date from circa 2500 B.C. The Indus civilisation is considered contemporary with the civilisation of Mesopotamia, which is said to be the oldest traced after Egypt. The Indus civilisation sites, which were excavated by the British during the *Raj*, are now considered some of the most important tourist attractions in Pakistan. Ironically, although the British 'created' this valuable tourist resource, they left Pakistan a terrible legacy in that they failed to adequately protect the ruins against disintegration, or alternatively to replace the protective earth covering after documentation, an important act in sound modern archaeology. The consequence is sadly that the exposed ruins are being destroyed by waterlogging and salinity [31,101] (see Appendix 4).

However the first popularly known invasion of the sub-continent of India by *Europeans* resulted from the overland invasion in the north by the Greeks under Alexander the Great in 326 B.C., and included the occupation for many decades of the North-West Frontier, Punjab and the Sind, and the whole Middle East otherwise at the time. Many Greek officers and mercenaries remained behind in India when Alexander departed with the bulk of his forces, and ruled little kingdoms on his behalf for some time, until they became assimilated. Alexander's occupation is still etched in the memory of most northern Indians, many of whom, and in particular the blue eyed fair skinned *Pathans*, proudly profess to be descended from him or his army. It was an invasion which legend has it, was even preceded centuries before by another Greek, one Dionysus, and later Heracles, who like Alexander, became known as Greek gods.[30] The northern town of Secunderabad is named after Alexander, the Greek warrior King of Greece. Another Greek invasion of lesser import is said to have occurred in 200 B.C.

From then until the time that Vasco da Gama of Portugal discovered the first sea route to India, reaching Calicut, on the Malabar coast, in 1498, during the reign of King Henry VII of England (1485 - 1509), there was little movement of *Europeans* to India. But Roman, Greek and other foreign merchants are said to have been established in South Indian markets in AD 100.[96] Vasco da Gama eventually became the first Portuguese viceroy in India in 1524. From that time *Europeans* sailed to and stayed to live in India, starting with the Portuguese, and followed by the Dutch, French, Danes, Swedes, Prussians, Flemish and British. Their interest was principally to acquire wealth, originally only through trade. Queen Elizabeth 1 of England (1558 - 1603) first granted a trading Charter to the British E.I.C. in 1600, during the reign of the greatest Moghul Emperor of the Indian Empire, Akbar the Great (1556 - 1605). The British eventually supplanted all the other nations in India, and eventually dominated the country, although some remnants of other *European* nations remained, and continued to make their impact on the country, especially the French. *Europeans* mixed freely with the Indians up to the end of the 18th century, with relatively little racial discrimination between the *Europeans* and their progeny the *Anglo-Indians*. This was so both socially and officially, until the British first began acquiring control of large tracts of the country through the East India Company, culminating in the formal British *Raj* over the whole Indian Empire in 1858, during the reign of Queen Victoria of England (1837 - 1901), (see Part 2).

4. Place of Domicile -

Apart from tea and indigo plantations, and remote outstations in the *mofussil*, the bulk of *Anglo-Indians* and *Domiciled Europeans* were concentrated in the major commercial cities and administrative capitals of British India, namely Delhi, Bombay (*Mumbai*), Calcutta *(Kolkata)*, and Madras *(Chennai)*, towns which were virtually created by the British *Raj*, except for the ancient capital of old Delhi. They were also found at the Military *cantonments* created by the British, at such towns as Rawalpindi, Ahmednagar, Allahabad, Peshawer, Quetta, Mhow, Ambala, Dum Dum, Bangalore, and Deolali (*Devlali*), Poona (*Pune*), and Kirkee (*Khadki*). Other concentrations of the community were at Railway centres created by the British when they built the railways in the 19th and 20th centuries, at such additional places as Jhansi, Jamalpur, Jubbulpore (*Jabalpur*), Ajmer, Chittaranjan, Byculla (Bombay), Parel (Bombay), Lonavla and Bhusaval, and scores more. There they lived mostly in flats in the big towns, and *bungalows* in the smaller stations, provided by their employers, and most commonly in close knit railway colonies, military *cantonments* or civil lines. These were areas of the towns away from the teeming native city, with its congested streets and *bazaars*. They were always laid out with wide tree-lined and surfaced roads, bordered with white-washed white stones, with large gated and fenced, or often walled compounds surrounding each bungalow. My own family were stationed mostly in Bombay, Bhusaval, Poona, and Kirkee, in both railway quarters and *cantonment* housing. Attempts were made to form separate *Anglo-Indian* colony states in India, in the 20th century, as at Whitfield, near Bangalore, Mogra, near Dehra Dun. The most ambitious of all was by E. T. McCluskie at McCluskieganj, near Ranchi. None were a great success.[32]

5. Way of Life -

The British in India were not colonists, as they were in the U.S.A., Canada and Australia. At first they considered England or, more correctly, the British Isles as Home and were originally only domiciled in India for the duration of their contracts. However many chose to stay on, most not returning Home very often. Home leave at intervals of ten to fifteen years was quite common. Many generations of *European* families were born in India, spent their lives there and ultimately died there. It was considered by most to be a good life. So in many respects they were settled in the country, though not as colonists. Colonial restrictions inhibited their integration into India. Consequentially they generally stood aloof from the native, and failed to take an interest in Indian life, culture and society, except where it impinged upon their immediate lives and employment, or when it suited them. Not that Indian strict religious and cultural customs were very helpful in this respect. Like the *Moghuls* the British were very tolerant towards the Indians, allowing them to carry on their way of life, including practising their own religions as they chose. The British lived in an artificial society of their own, quite separate from the Indians. An English clone society, with trimmings, especially in the way of numerous native servants, to remove the drudgery of life, including the cooking, washing-up, cleaning the house, washing and ironing, bathing and minding the children, gardening and driving the car. In many respects they led a far higher lifestyle on average than many would have enjoyed at Home, and consequently they had the opportunity to enjoy life to the full.

But like all transplants, *Europeans* had their problems, which apart from the perpetual dust and dirt, flies, insects, scorpions and snakes, the fear of disease and endemic sickness, and the proliferation of languages and customs, was perhaps boredom, or the fear of it, especially for the women. In an essentially man's world it was the women who suffered the most. The men were occupied on engrossing work all day, with responsibilities far and above those normal at Home to challenge them. Their spare time was spent in the religious pursuit of sport, with hockey, cricket, tennis and polo amongst others, and the inevitable *shikar*, with a wide selection of game birds from swarms of partridge to flocks of green pigeon, and innumerable animals from the majestic tiger to sleek black buck, to choose from. Few at that time were concerned about wild life conservation, needless to say. The early evenings saw relaxation in the company of other men enjoying a whisky *burra* peg at the *European* club, whilst discussing usually work, or the latest or next shoot, or sporting activity. But women's activities were less absorbing, as housekeeping was taken care of by servants, and there was a limit to social calls and shopping, especially in remote stations. An obsessive interest was taken by the *memsahibs* in checking individually the contents of the daily purchases of food from the *bazaar* by the Indian cook, who was capable of cleverly memorising the exact cost of perhaps 25 items displayed on a commodious tray, whilst he concealed his normal *dustoorie* (commission). There was also the twice weekly items of washing removed by the *dhobi*, to beat to extinction on rocks at the nearby *dhobi ghat*. Children were generally farmed off to boarding school either in Britain, or depending on circumstances in India. But contrary to the impression given in literature, the majority of *Anglo-Indians* and *Domiciled European* children were sent to one of the more than two hundred excellent schools in India, and not just to the albeit splendid schools in the foothills of the Himalayas, just as soon as they were weaned. I myself was sent 500 miles away to the Jesuit St. Joseph's College, Bangalore in 1937, just 6 years old. Later with outbreak of the Second World War in 1939 I was transferred to Barnes High School Deolali, only 150 miles away, apart for a brief period at Shri Shivaji Preparatory Military School in Poona, when the threat of Japanese invasion of India was upon us, (see Appendix 2). In most cases before then children were under the total care of an *ayah*. Conversations at coffee or tea with other women generally revolved around inefficient servants, the latest arrivals in the *cantonment*, or the weather, although the latter was not as common a subject as back Home, as the weather was in contrast totally predictable. Many wives unfortunately found solace in drink in consequence, and not just at the club dances on a Saturday night, which were as equally well attended as church service on Sunday. Others were drawn towards church activities, or engaged in extra-marital liaisons, though usually only with fellow *Europeans*, or *Anglo-Indians* of the opposite sex, of which the British and American military, during the Second World War, provided many willing participators. Many single and some married women, especially during the war, were able to engage in employment, or voluntary work, with the post office, armed services, major *European* businesses, or as governesses to wealthy Indian families.

Very few *Europeans* and *Anglo-Indians* owned their own homes in India. They were in general rented, and mostly from the government services or companies who employed them. Also relatively little land was owned, unlike other British colonies. Some acquired small areas of land in the early years of the British *Raj* or before, sometimes through marriage into wealthy Indian families. Until 1837 the E.I.C. prohibited *Europeans* from directly owning land. Small areas were subsequently acquired by indigo, tea and jute *European* planters, growing arguably the finest products in the world, the latter being almost a world monopoly. Urban and industrial properties were also acquired. Many owned successful businesses, although this was often in partnership with Indians. Mostly the early *Europeans* and many *Anglo-Indians* too, not in the army, made their fortunes through trading.

Apart from the mandatory attendance of school classes, a child's life was perhaps the best, as it is all over the world. There was always plenty of organised sport on hand of course during school terms, such as hockey, cricket, football, athletics, swimming and boxing, which were usually compulsory. However after hours, or school holidays, was usually more interesting, when children engaged in more free sports, some of native origin, or wandered the wide open plains and jungles of India, free and easy, like Mark Twain's 'Adventure's of Huckleberry Finn' [90] fishing freely with home made rods in the many rivers and lakes, shooting and trapping birds, and collecting bird eggs and butterflies for collections, or just caring for orphaned, or injured wild birds and animals as pets.

The British in India were very proud of their nationality and their British heritage, even more so it seemed at times than people back Home in England. They were forever lauding their fair legal system, their proud military record and their manufacturing prowess. In a land where bribery and corruption was endemic, and a recognised way of life amongst the natives, they were respected for being above reproach. Before Indian Independence anything with 'Made in England' on it was always the best, 'U.S.' made was useless and 'Made in Japan' meant trash. This of course is no longer the case. Then, the British accepted that history had made Great Britain the paramount nation of the world and 'master' race in the Indian sub-continent, and they paraded themselves with considerable confidence, and were hugely successful in what they achieved in consequence. The Indians accepted this domination with surprising good grace, on the surface, until the Indian Mutiny of 1857, and the start of Indian Nationalism in the early 20th century, fanned by the non-violent opposition campaigns of the nationally respected *Mahatma* Gandhi in later years. The common man in India still respects the English, I discovered in the 1960's and in 1995 when I returned there, and not just any white people as some suppose, and they look back to the days of the British *Raj* with affection. There was common respect and trust, especially with the lower strata of Indian society, such as were used by the *Europeans* in subordinate positions or as domestic servants. There was no latent fear by the British of molestation, or rape by the numerous servants in every household, nor whilst visiting the *bazaars* unaccompanied. Nor was there any risk of child abuse either, such as is allegedly commonplace in the west today. Infant children were cared for and taken out daily for walks in the *cantonment* and civil lines, in the company only of an *ayah*. The older children, although more particularly the boys, were free to roam the countryside and city *bazaar* unattended and unmolested.

The English were in consequence very proud to be both *European* and white, the latter being their exterior badge of superiority. Any suggestion that they were otherwise, or that they might have the slightest 'lick of the tar brush' (that is with some native blood) brought a very swift and angry rebuttal. It was considered a grave insult. Frank Anthony, the leader of the *Anglo-Indians* in India post-independence, was of the opinion that most *European* families who had been in India for several generations, would more than likely have some Indian blood anyway, either through marital wedlock, or premarital or extra-marital indiscretions otherwise, sometimes cleverly concealed where the child had been fortunate to be born fair.[2] It used to be a common source of amusement amongst the British of Bombay, that there were many young 'look-a-likes' of the British Prince of Wales wandering the streets, in the years following the future King Edward VII's tour of India in 1875.

Although a considerable number of people emigrated from the British Isles in the 19th and early 20th centuries, by far the majority sailed for the United States of America (where land could be settled), both before and after American Independence in 1776. Relatively few emigrated to the colonies of the British Empire until the middle of the 20th century, and those generally to the colonies of white settlement, mostly by choice to Canada, and initially only under criminal sentence to Australia. In general, *Europeans* themselves were not allowed legitimately to own large tracts of land in India, as the East India Company feared that their successful colonisation would interfere with their trading monopoly. But the native wives of *Europeans* could, and many adventurers were to take advantage of this to acquire large estates, but only on a very small overall scale, as compared with other Crown colonies. Movement of persons to India, apart from covenanted posts themselves, consisted almost entirely of their families, who in most cases were to become *Domiciled Europeans* ultimately, mostly engaged in government or government-related service. A smaller number entered commerce, known disparagingly as 'box-wallahs'. The name was probably derived from the more humble but very well mannered and well dressed *bories* or India traders, and Chinese traders (all called 'John') , who with boxes or huge bundles, on the rear carriers of bicycles, peddled their wonderful wares from house to house, and gave the *memsahibs* much pleasure and the *sahibs* much extra '*bazaaring*' (spending money) to find. The *Domiciled Europeans* who decided to stay on in India at retirement, which was generally at about aged 50 or 55 years of age, often settled in the popular hill stations such as Simla (*Shimla*) and Mussoorie in the Himalayan foothills of north India, and Bangalore and Ootacamund in south India, where the climate was more refreshing.

6. Protected Status -

When the Portuguese, and in their turn the Dutch, were forced to evacuate their possessions in India by right of conquest, in the 17th and 18th centuries respectively, special clauses were written in to the deeds of surrender to protect the interests of their mixed races. These provisions were adhered to during the British *Raj*, with a large number of the middle ranking operational posts in the Railways, Telegraph and Customs and Excise and Police being filled by *Anglo-Indians*, and including *Luso Indians*, right up to Indian independence in 1947. After Independence, although places continued to be reserved for them, the indigenous Indians became the majority. The advent of these former services was especially beneficial to the *Anglo-Indian* Community and through them the British were well served. Large numbers were also recruited into the ranks of armies of the British in India, and into the uncovenanted civil service. However most middle ranking posts were still reserved for *Domiciled Europeans*, who had to prove they were domiciled first, an extremely difficult exercise for families domiciled in India for generations.

Where a father could afford it, *Domiciled European* and *Anglo-Indian* children were sent Home to England for education, from whence they returned to covenanted and commissioned civil or military service with the E.I.C., and later the Crown and with great success. But this was not always so. And furthermore, the majority could not afford this expense, and were educated locally in India, at over 200 boarding and numerous private, Railway and Army English speaking *Anglo-Indian* day schools already mentioned. Although these were generally of a very high standard, comparable with public schools back Home, they were discriminated against for the better government posts. Contrary to popular belief arguably more British children were educated in India, than were sent Home to Britain, although the majority of these were *Anglo-Indian* (see Appendix 2).

7. Discrimination -

Towards the end of the 18th century, the *Anglo-Indians*, who outnumbered the *Europeans* in India, began to succeed in all walks of military and civilian life, where up until then there was no prejudice against them. Their success was partly to blame for the repressive measures instituted against them by the British, following the white mutiny in 1766 in the army of the E.I.C. under Robert Clive, who was referred to by some as the founder of the British *Raj*, after his victory at the battle of Plassey in 1757. The E.I.C. feared a general rebellion spear-headed by *Anglo-Indians* in India, such as occurred with the mixed blood *mullatoes* in the former Spanish American colonies of Haiti and San Domingo, in the West Indies. They also feared the increasing competition from *Anglo-Indians* for senior posts in the civil and military services, normally reserved for the sons of *European* share holders of the East India Company. By a Company decree in 1792 '*No Person, the son of a native Indian, shall henceforth be appointed by this Court to appointments in the Civil, Military or Marine services of the country.*' The opportunities of the *Anglo-Indians* for education and training in England were curtailed. They were discharged from civil and military service, and forbidden from acquiring land and from residing further than 10 miles from a presidency town, or Company settlement. This latter effectively debarring them from agriculture or trading. They were ultimately used as pawns in the process of colonisation.They were conscripted back into the British Army under threat of treason at times of emergency, such as to combat marauding native armies during the Mysore and *Maratha* Wars, (including for example the battle against the *Marathas* of 1802 at Poona, where ironically Lieut. General Sir Richard Jones,[42] the Commander in Chief of the Bombay Army was an *Anglo-Indian).* On conclusion of the emergencies these unfortunate *Anglo-Indians* were then summarily discharged, without recourse to continuing employment, nor compensation. There were other exceptions to the exclusion also, for senior and respected *Anglo-Indians* already in service at the time, such as the Quartermaster-General of the Army Colonel Stevenson, and the renowned

Colonel James Skinner, of Skinner's Horse fame (see later), and many more in the King's army, together with the medical and numerous other civil professions.

In 1817 the *Anglo-Indian Community* (or *'East Indians'* as they then preferred to call themselves), delivered a petition to the Governor-General, the Marquis of Hastings, in an attempt to improve their lot in India, but with no response from local government, nor the East India Company. Eventually in 1830 John William Ricketts, Deputy-Registrar of the Board of Revenue, and the *Anglo-Indian* son of an Ensign in the Bengal Engineers, one of the leaders of the *Anglo-Indian* community in Calcutta, was deputed to present a petition of grievances respecting official prejudice against the community, to the British Parliament, with some subsequent success. Herbert Stark, once President of the *'Anglo-Indian and Domiciled European Association of Bengal'*, related in his book *'John Ricketts and His Times'*,[84] how Ricketts brought it to the notice of Parliament, that whilst it was considered respectable for a large proportion of the *European* officers at the time, of the East India Company, to marry *Anglo-Indian* girls (and sometimes they were only girls in their lower teens from military orphanages) the *Anglo-Indian* men were, since 1792, forbidden from taking senior jobs in civil or military service of both the Company and the Crown, which were open to the British. They were also made ineligible for subordinate posts, such as Judicial, Revenue and Police and Military service, made unreservedly open to the *Muslims* and *Hindus* of the country, except for Drums and Fyffes in the military. Up until then *Anglo-Indians* had been welcome and succeeded on merit both senior and subordinate positions in these services.

John Ricketts also brought to the notice of Parliament that *Anglo-Indians* were not recognised as *European* by the British, nor as Indian by the Indians, and so ended up falling between two stools in the courts. They did not enjoy the total legal rights and protection of the British within the British territories, where British law prevailed, in that they were not allowed a jury. They were also not covered by British civil laws, respecting births, deaths, marriages, and inheritance. Also as Christians they were debarred from the adoption of *Muslim* or *Hindu* civil law. When they ventured into the Indian territories not ruled by the British, they also had no recourse to the protection afforded to British nationals there, and were in consequence liable to the harsher criminal laws of the ruling *Muslims* or *Hindus*. They were in effect outlaws and all but stateless, in both the country of their birth and blood.[1,84]

By the Charter Act 1833 the character of the East India Company was changed from that of *'merchants and traders, to an administrative government, in whose impartial eyes all subjects had equality of rights and privileges; so that neither birth, religion nor colour was any longer a help or hindrance to admission into the civil and military services of the State'*. These recommendations were given effect by the Indian legislature in 1836, whereby ' *the Laws of England as interpreted and enforced in British Courts of Justice in India, would henceforth apply in the Company's Possessions'*. It provided that the ' *law would thenceforth be impartial to all classes, creeds and races. Preferential treatment hitherto accorded to Europeans would cease'*. In 1835 English replaced Persian as the official language in India of government, courts and offices, which was a great boost to the prospects of employment of the *Anglo-Indians*, whose native tongue was English, when in competition with the Indian *Muslims* and *Hindus*. But discrimination continued.[84]

8. Social Precedence -

A strict order of social precedence was observed by the *Europeans* at all times, and in all places in British India, often stricter than to be found back Home; a development which was understood and encouraged by the Indians, who observed a very strict and discriminatory social caste system of their own. *The Simla Government issued an elaborate Warrant of Precedence with 63 ranks - the Viceroy at the top and a superintendent of a telegraph workshop at the bottom. It included military as well as civil ranks.'* [18] Needless to say the *Anglo-Indians* were at the bottom of the scale, as indeed were many *Domiciled Europeans* during the *Raj*.

9. Sea Passages -

Sea passages to India from Europe, then around the South African Cape of Good Hope, took six months and were very costly, amounting to £200 to £300, and as much as £500 for a lady, until 1835.   The shorter partially overland route across Europe and Egypt was then discovered to India, to be followed in 1869 by a shorter cheaper route, with the opening of the Suez Canal. This canal connecting the Mediterranean to the Red Sea was a gigantic Civil Engineering achievement (see Part 2), which reduced the journey to India ultimately to only 2 to 3 weeks and cost considerably less than before, amounting to as little as £31 in 1891 when my great grandfather sailed for India. As a consequence many more *European* men took advantage of this opportunity to seek their fortunes in India, competing successfully for employment with the *Anglo-Indians*, as their services were more favoured. Furthermore, more single *European* women (known as the 'fishing fleet') seeking eligible wealthy husbands and the *European* wives of expatriates, travelled to India. Soon liaisons with native Indians and *Anglo-Indian* women began to be condemned, or considered immoral by *Europeans*.   These developments did great harm to the reputation and opportunities of the *Anglo-Indian Community*. The *European* population in India trebled to 126,000 between the 1830's and 1860's.[18]

10. Impact of the Railways -

This unhappy chapter of discrimination against the *Anglo-Indian* community did not terminate until the mid-nineteenth century with the advent in India of the Telegraph in 1851 and the Railways, with the first railway from Bombay to Thana opening in 1853 (see Appendix 3). Then the *Anglo-Indian* Community came into their own in providing reliable skilled and semi skilled staff and labour. The railway communities were also able to show their worth and loyalty to the Crown during the Indian Mutiny of 1857, especially in the Ganges valley where the mutinous Indian soldiers exacted terrible slaughter of British soldiers and civilians, and attempted to sabotage the railways (see Part 2).

With the advent of the Telegraph and Railways many *European* skilled craftsmen, Civil Engineers and supervisory staff were recruited into India from the British Isles. They received double their Home pay to hold them, and were used to reinforce the splendid Military Engineers already engaged in the construction and supervision of these colossal Engineering ventures, said to be the largest systems in the world. Subsequently they were retained on the operation and maintenance of the permanent way, engines, rolling stock and workshop plant and machinery, and were responsible for training of the local people. Many stayed on in India when their English contracts of service expired and even died there in service. The *European* contractor's construction gangers and foremen were said to be '*hard-working, hard-drinking, and reckless*'. The turnover of expatriate staff was high, death and incapacitating sickness alone removing five percent of them each year. Many others were recruited from *European* British soldiers taking their discharge in India. These expatriates were responsible for a new wave of *Domiciled European* families in the country, and the start of further *Anglo-Indian* expansion.[100]

The Railway's best pupils for training were found from amongst the then existing *Anglo-Indians* who had inherited the English language and their mechanical aptitude from their *European* forbears.[2] In 1915 the Railways employed 600,000 workers, consisting of 8000 *Europeans*, 10,000 *Anglo-Indians* and 582,000 Indians.[100] Up until 1920 practically all the positions of guards, engine drivers, station masters and permanent way inspectors on the railways were held initially by covenanted *Europeans* and subsequently by *Domiciled Europeans* or *Anglo-Indians*. Posts of Railway General Managers (once known as Agents), Chief Engineers and General Traffic Managers were usually occupied by *Covenanted Europeans* and later *Domiciled Europeans only*, with some fair *Anglo-Indians* masquerading as *Europeans*. After this more Indians were allowed into the service. By 1926 *Europeans* held only 70 percent of superior posts and *Anglo-Indians* 8 percent. Out of a total of about 763,000 railway employees, 14,000 were *Anglo-Indian*. These percentage numbers of *Anglo-Indians* were protected by the government until 1947, after which reservations decreased, until protection was removed in 1960. The same was the case with the Irrigation Department, Post and Telegraph, Custom and Excise, Police, Forestry, and Indian Medical Services.[2] My great grandfather was a Foreman Boilersmith, and his son a Foreman Engineering Fitter in the G.I.P.R., at the turn of the century. Another was an Apothecary in the I.M.D.. An uncle was an inspector in the Bombay Police in the late 1940's.

The railways covered the whole country and extended to 40,500 miles, and included such pioneering companies as the Great Indian Peninsula Railway (G.I.P.R.) and Madras Railway (M.R.), later to become the Madras and Southern Maratha Railway (M.S.M.R.) in the Deccan, the East Indian Railway (E.I.R.) and the Bombay Baroda and Central Indian Railway, (B.B.&C.I.R.), amongst many others. The Railway system was the greatest of the many great legacies the British left to India and Pakistan at their independence in 1947 (see Appendix 3).

Similar great Engineering ventures followed in Road building and Irrigation works. The primitive *Moghul* Grand Trunk Road, extending 1500 miles from Calcutta to Peshawer, was developed into the first safe all-weather arterial road in the country. The Lloyd Barrage irrigation scheme, with its mile long barrage across the River Indus at Sukkur in the Sind, completed in 1932, was the largest in the world and probably the greatest single project constructed by the British in India (see Appendix 4).

11. Self Government Threat-

Since the Indian Mutiny of 1857 and the formation of the Indian National Congress in 1885, great concern began to be felt by the *Domiciled Europeans* and *Anglo-Indians* of the Indian sub-continent, about their future position and status, in the event of India achieving self government. In 1880 the restrictions to employment of *Anglo-Indians* in senior government service were lifted and places previously filled by middle class British direct from Britain was restricted to persons who were *'Indians by statutory law.'* [83] This was of considerable help to both the *Anglo-Indian* and *Domiciled European* communities. However, it was not always observed, as posts as late as 1926 were still reserved for *Domiciled Europeans* only, for which a fair skin was inadequate proof and domicile had to be established first. By the *Government of India Act 1919*, the *Anglo-Indian* Community was officially recognised and given special representation in both the Central and Provincial Legislatures of the Indian Government. An *Anglo-Indian* was described as

> ' *Every person, being a British subject and resident in British India, of*
> *(a) European descent in the male line who is not comprised in the above definition, or*
> *(b) mixed Asiatic descent, whose father, grandfather or remote ancestor in the male line was born in the continent of Europe, Canada, Newfoundland, Australia, New Zealand, the Union of South Africa or the United States of America, and who is not entered in the European electoral roll. '* [83]

However the pace of Indianisation accelerated after the 1919 Act and both *Anglo-Indians* and *Domiciled Europeans* found their employment threatened by more Indians being employed in positions previously reserved for them. Efforts to overcome this were eventually made by leading representatives of the community, commencing with Herbert Alick Stark, author of *'Hostages to India'*,[83] a member of the Education Department and the first *Anglo-Indian* Inspector of *European* schools, who led a deputation to London in 1923. This was followed in 1925 by another headed by the then leader of the *Anglo-Indian Community*, the accomplished I.M.D. Ophthalmic Surgeon, Sir Henry Gidney,[93] The Government stated incredulously that '*For the purpose of employment under Government and inclusion in schemes of Indianisation, members of the Anglo-Indian and Domiciled European community are statutory natives of India. For the purposes of education and internal security, their status, in so far as it admits of definition, approximates to that of European British subjects.*' [73] Gidney's father, who lost his life in the Indian Mutiny was an Englishman who married a lady of mixed Spanish and *Eurasion* descent, who was once employed in the G.I.P. Railway at Igatpuri east of Bombay. Gidney had in 1919 supplanted J.H.Abbot, the President-in-Chief of the *Anglo-Indian Empire League*, the foremost of the numerous associations which represented the *Anglo-Indian Community* in India then, which he headed for 22 years. Gidney made great efforts to get the somewhat provincial and fragmented *Anglo-Indian Community* to amalgamate to form one united and representative organisation to look after the interests of the community. This he did in 1926 with the inauguration of the *Anglo-Indian and Domiciled European Association, All-India and Burma*, with 88 branches all over India. Other pioneer *Anglo-Indian* leaders of the time were E.W.Chambers, Kenneth Wallace, W.C.Madge, and later E.T.McCluskie (Real Estate Agent), L.T.Maguire (Lawyer) and Dr. Pushong (MD).[1,2]

The *Government of India Act 1935* did nothing to quell the fears and anxieties of the *Anglo-Indian* Community, as reference was only made to *Europeans* and *Anglo-Indians*, the label *Domiciled European* not being used.[83] The *Anglo-Indian* was defined as, '*A person whose father or any of whose other male progenitors in the male line is or was of European descent but who is a native of India.*' In 1949 the Indian Constitution accepted this definition of *Anglo-Indian*. A native of India meant '*one who is born and domiciled in India, of parents primarily resident in India and not established here for temporary purposes only, in contrast to the European who comes to India for a term, short or long, of his life.*' [32]

12. The Military and War Service -

The military in India was always a great source of employment. The military posts in British India were filled by people from all walks of life, although it usually mattered who you knew, for the more ambitious. The army of E.I.C., or John Company as it is also known, grew like topsy, from somewhat haphazard beginnings consisting of Indian factory guard detachments with a single gunner, and local militia in the 1600s, to become immense armies of horse, foot and artillery at the time of Lord Robert Clive of Plassey in 1757, (see Part 2). The first *European* companies were said to have been made up of the flotsam and jetsam of *European* humanity in India. Later they were supported by King's troops from England. Up until just before the final defeat of the French in 1793 the *Anglo-Indians* were treated as equals and held senior commands in the army, but as a result of the E.I.C. decree of 1792, see earlier, they were all discharged. They were subsequently only allowed posts as bandsmen during peaceful intervals, and were conscripted on pain of charge of treachery at times of war, such as against the *Marathas* in the 1800s. In consequence many *Anglo-Indians* offered their services to the Indian Princes instead, see later. At this time there were only 13,000 *European* soldiers in India, including both King's and E.I.C.. There were about 24,000 Indian troops in each of Bengal and Madras armies and 9,000 in Bombay.[53] The position was not to improve until about 1880, by which time the E.I.C. army was disbanded in favour of the Indian Army, which commenced after the Indian Mutiny in 1857. The British, or King's Army, which had reinforced the E.I.C. Army, remained intact.

The British Armies in India after the Mutiny consisted of the British Army, which included all the artillery, and the much larger Indian Army, which operated in parallel. Officers in the British Army, where all ranks were *European*, were required to purchase their commission, that is the King's commission, until 1870. These positions usually went to people of middle and upper middle class origin, who could afford the expensive Sandhurst training and the purchase. King's Commissions were also available to British *Europeans* free, with the same military training, but on merit, in the Indian Army (B.O.). It was considered more valuable to their owners, as promotion depended on meritorious service and 'dead man's shoes', resulting frequently in officers with more service experience than their counterparts in the British Army, although older officers in consequence.

Apart from the excitement enjoyed by most in active service, prospects were always better for promotion. It was however considered useful in both services for officers to have a private income to supplement their pay, to accommodate their generally expensive social and sporting lifestyle. There was always great rivalry between the two services, and between the individual regiments of each. The Commander-in-Chief was until the latter years of the *Raj* always from the British Army.[9,57] King's commissions were also opened to suitably trained Indians in the Indian Army after World War 1, when some went to Sandhurst and Woolwich and were commissioned as King's Indian commissioned officers (K.I.C.O.). Later in 1932 after the Indian Military Academy was opened at Dehra Dun, officers commissioned there were known as Indian commissioned officers (I.C.O.). Viceroy's commissions (V.C.O.) were also available free to junior status Indian officers in the Indian Army, selected on merit and years of service. They were in consequence more mature than their fellow *European* officers of apparent similar rank.

All non-commissioned officers (N.C.O.) and other ranks were usually Indian in the Indian Army, although there frequently were *European* N.C.O.s transferred from the British Army, to assist training in the early days. All non-commissioned officers and common soldiers in the British Army were *European*. They had few privileges, and were treated very harshly, worse than Indian troops, especially in Victorian times, where discipline was brutal, death-rate very high and pay very poor, and were generally recruited from the British working classes for a minimum of 21 years until 1870 for the regular army, after which it was reduced to 12 years. *Domiciled Europeans* and fair *Anglo-Indians* clearly had an advantage over their darker brothers in obtaining a King's commission (B.O.) in the Indian Army. Those who failed could still apply for a K.I.C.O. commission, if they were prepared to face it. Officers, N.C.O.s, and other ranks in the British Army were usually recruited in England. I have many ancestors who were N.C.O.s and B.O.R.s in the E.I.C. Army and British Army in India. The Regiments they were in, included the Bombay (later Royal) Fusiliers, Bombay *European* Regiment, Royal Artillery, 3rd Dragoon Guards, 18th Hussars, and Royal Horse Artillery. My father was a Sergeant in the 2nd Dorset Regiment, in Mesopotamia in the Great War.

During the Great War (World War 1) of 1914-1918 and World War 2 of 1939-1945, *Anglo-Indians* were considered as *Europeans* for the British and Indian Armies, the Royal Navy and the Royal Air Force. They acquitted themselves as well as they had also done in earlier occasions during the Afghan Wars and battles on the North-West Frontier against the fearsome *Pathans* and other mountain tribesmen, winning many battle honours and rising to senior posts in all the services. The Indian Army was expanded from 200,000 to 2.5 million men, entirely by voluntary enlistment, during the World War 2, an indication of the loyalty, courage and pride of the people of the British Indian Empire. About 8,000 *Anglo-Indians* were supposed to have enlisted in World War 1 as *Europeans* in British regiments, including a large number in the Dorset Regiment, which saw action in Mesopotamia. The *Anglo-Indians* themselves were allowed to raise two Field Troops of Cavalry, a section of the Field Artillery and 16 platoons of infantry. The *Anglo-Indian* Battery was attached to the 77th Royal Field Artillery. A Volunteer Artillery Battalion was also raised in Burma. They all also saw action in Mesopotamia.[2] *Anglo-Indians* overrun by the occupation of Burma by the Japanese contributed greatly to the eventual defeat of them, as did those in the services in South East Asia Command (S.E.A.C.) in World War 2. About 75 percent of the available manpower of the *Anglo-Indian* Community in the Indian sub-continent are said to have joined the armed forces during World War 2, with a high percentage becoming officers in the Indian Army, the Royal Indian Navy (R.I.N.), and the Royal Indian Airforce (R.I.A.F.) also. There were others in the Royal Army Signalling Corps (R.A.S.C.), Royal Army Ordnance Corps (R.A.O.C.), Royal Engineers (R.E.), Royal Electrical & Mechanical Engineers (R.E.M.E.) and Royal Army Medical Corps (R.A.M.C.). At least 90 percent of *European* Emergency Commissioned Officers recruited in India are said to have been Anglo-Indians. Three of my uncles were in the Royal Engineers.

Some 2,000 to 3,000 *Anglo-Indians* were said to have served in the R.A.F. during the Battle of Britain and elsewhere. One of my brothers in law was a Flying Officer in the R.A.F. in India during the World War 2. About 70 to 80 percent of the St. John's Ambulance, Women's Auxiliary Corps (India) (W.A.C.(I.)), Indian Military Nursing Service (I.M.N.S.), Auxiliary Nursing Service (A.N.S.) and the Women's Voluntary Service (W.V.S.), (before they were made Royal), were women from the *Anglo-Indian* Community.[2] Many were also in the Queen Alexander's Imperial Military Nursing Service (known as Q.A.), First Aid Nursing Yeomanry (known as F.A.N.Y.), the Women's Auxiliary Nursing Service (Burma) (known as W.A.S.B.), who did sterling service during the war. My elder sister was a Subaltern in the W.A.C.(I.) in Lahore, and my mother was in the W.V.S. in Kirkee. The remainder of the joint community were active otherwise during World War 2, in the desperate struggle to run and maintain the ageing railways, telegraph and other essential services, such as the Ordnance and Medical services.

The *Anglo-Indian* and *Domiciled European* Community were persuaded after the Mutiny to form an army Volunteer Corps, later known as the Indian Defence Force (I.D.F.) and subsequently as the Auxiliary Force (India) or A.F.I. in 1920, as a form of civil defence or 'Home Guard', which numbered about 29,000 in 1939, and was disbanded in 1947. It was made up of several hundred units at most major towns and railway centres, such as the Poona Rifles and the Great Indian Peninsula Railway Regiment. In all the *Anglo-Indian* schools it was made a condition of eligibility for subsequent employment in government service, and in particular on the Railways, where most worked. This was an indirect way of the British Government both guaranteeing the allegiance of the *Anglo-Indians*, and ensuring that a loyal trained force of volunteers (a loyalty which need hardly have been questioned), was available to assist in any emergency involving the indigenous natives, and ensure that the *European* population would never again be entirely defenceless. To this end their formation was a great success, during the World Wars 1 and 2, when the country was denuded of British troops. They were also much used during the '*Quit India*' civil disobedience, and during sectarian riots of the 1930s and 1940s. I was recruited into the A.F.I. (G.I.P.R.Regiment) in 1946 in my last year at Barnes High School, Deolali. My father, who was in a reserved occupation in the Royal Ordnance Small Arms Factory in Kirkee, belonged to a Volunteer Corps called the 'Frontiersmen'. My maternal grandfather had also been employed there just prior to the war, and two uncles were there during the war also.

13. Persecution -

Although both *Domiciled European* and *Anglo-Indian* communities were British Subjects during the *Raj*, all *Europeans* in India regardless were inclined to look down upon *Anglo-Indians* as being half castes, and thus inferior. They claimed more right to British Citizenship, or English, Welsh, Scottish or Irish nationality, by virtue of their white skin and pure *European* expatriate blood. *Anglo-Indians'* skin colour can differ from white to almost black, occasionally in a single family. They usually spoke English, as their native tongue, but with an accent described locally as 'Bombay Welsh', because it had a sing-song sound similar to the Welsh dialect. It happens many *Domiciled Europeans* also spoke similarly, often a giveaway to their early lives in India. A description of the inter-relationship between *Europeans, Anglo-Indians* and Indians in India in general in 1946, is graphically described in the fictional book *'Bhowani Junction'*, by the late John Masters,[56] an *Anglo-Indian* himself. A very realistic and atmospheric film of the same name, which starred Stewart Grainger, Ava Gardner and Bill Travers, was based on the book. The depiction of the *Anglo-Indians* as oafish and promiscuous in both the book and film, was considered most offensive by the *Anglo-Indian* Community. A commonly known, though derogatory limerick, quoted in this book went as follows:-

> *'There was a young lady called Starkie,*
> *Who had an affair with a darkie,*
> *The results of her sins*
> *Was an eightsome of twins-*
> *Two black and two white and four khaki'.*

Anglo-Indians were discriminated against and treated like second class British Subjects in India, including being excluded from membership of the *burra European* clubs, such as the Bombay Gymkhana, that renowned British institution and symbol of life in the colonies. However some with a fair skin were able to obtain membership, by masquerading as *European*. This shameful discrimination was fortunately not applied in the smaller provincial clubs, such as the Ordnance Clubs in military *cantonments*, such as at Kirkee, near Poona. The Poona Club was *'open to European and Indian gentlemen'*, according to Taraporevala, in his *'Up-to-Date Guide to Poona'*,[87] although doubtless selectively, and by inference *Anglo-Indians* too. However the Club of Western India in the 'Camp' he says was exclusively *European* in 1934. It is interesting to note his mention of *'The Poona Hunt:--the Oldest Tent Club in India, having been started in 1815.'* [86]. I spent a holiday from school in 1945 with an aunt who lived next door to the hound kennels on the Sholapur Road. There were of course no foxes to hunt, but jackals were a good substitute. In the early years of the hunt the quarry was wild boar.[80] The *Anglo-Indians* did of course have their own clubs, especially the popular railway institutes, attended also by *Domiciled Europeans*. Separate establishments were provided for Indians. This racial prejudice, or inclination to not recognise *Anglo-Indians* as *pukka sahibs*, from both the *Europeans* and the Indians alike, was uncalled for, especially from the British, as almost all *Anglo-Indians* considered England their Home also. Furthermore, they were almost exclusively Christian, the majority religion of Europe, and their mother tongue and life-style was generally English. The more snobbish *Europeans* would not associate socially with *Anglo-Indians*, and did not consider them as trustworthy as *Europeans*, nor often even as Indians.

Many *Europeans* were anxious about their children forming amorous attachments with *Anglo-Indians*, even though they were superficially white, or apparently *European*, as any subsequent generation could be coloured. There was an inclination to ensure this, by taking note of the colour of the cuticles of the fingernails of suspected *Anglo-Indians*, which differ from *Europeans* in colour. Pale eye colour alone was also no certain proof of pure *European* blood. After all some *Pathans* of the North

West Frontier were said to have fair eyes. Unfortunately the concern became so bigoted with some *Europeans*, that they even shunned fair people who were, or whose parents were, employed in junior positions on the railways, telegraphs and other main government services, where the majority *Anglo-Indians* were employed, although not exclusively, assuming them all to be *Anglo-Indians*. *Europeans* who chose to marry Indians, or *Anglo-Indians*, were often ostracised by the more bigoted *European*, sometimes to even excluding them, or their partners totally from *European* society, clubs, or important occasions. This state of affairs only really began after the commencement of official British rule in 1858.

This prejudice against *Anglo-Indians* was more prevalent amongst high class Indians, and British fresh from Home, known as 'griffins', ' *a white person new to the East; recently come from the Occident'* 97 unaware of proper colonial social behaviour in India, than with the *Domiciled European*, who lived and worked amongst, and went to school locally with *Anglo-Indians*. Conversely *European* children sometimes suffered mental and physical persecution in reverse, from the more populous *Anglo-Indians* with whom they shared schools and recreational facilities, just for claiming to be *European*. I can remember being teased in school in this way. *European memsahibs* and British troops were considered the worst offenders of stigmatising the *Anglo-Indians*. *Anglo-Indians* were often, though not commonly, called or referred to by derogatory and uncomplimentary names, like 'anglo-banglo', 'half-caste', 'blackie-white', 'lick of the tar brush', 'wogs', 'nigger', *'char anna'*, or *'chi-chi'*, alluding to their being of mixed blood, or to their colour being off-white, and also sometimes referring to their characteristic English sing-song accent. To children, the word *'chi chi'* also signified dirty. *'Char anna'*, equal to a quarter of a *rupee* only, alluded to their fraction of *European* blood. The name was also used when referring to young *Anglo-Indian* women, and was a scandalous reference to their alleged sexual promiscuity. They were claimed to have an appetite particularly for white men, a supposed ambition to claim *European* nationality by association, and to mother fairer children. It has to be remembered that there were not many *European* eligible young ladies in the country, available to be courted, and not just by the fairly numerous British 'Tommies' (soldiers). Besides, *Anglo-Indian* girls are generally very attractive. The result of the mixed marriages usually resulted in a handsome and respectable race of people, who mostly led good Christian lives, and tried to live up to what they thought to be their English heritage.

14. Life after Independence

At Indian independence in 1947 all subjects of the British *Raj* and indeed of the British Empire, that is *European*, 'country-born' or native, were considered 'British Subjects' and had equal rights to residence at Home. In anticipation of India becoming a republic, British domestic law was changed with the *'British Nationality Act 1948'*11,39 (effective from 1st January 1949), which dissolved common citizenship of the British

Commonwealth and Empire. This was replaced by *'British Subject, Citizen of the United Kingdom and Colonies'* for residents of the United Kingdom, and the remaining few colonies ruled from Whitehall; and the remainder of *'British Subjects'* became *'Commonwealth Citizens'* in British parlance. *Anglo-Indians* were required to prove British European descent in the original male line, usually their paternal grandfathers. Britain did not at first restrict entry of *Commonwealth Citizens* into Britain, but eventually did when the *'Commonwealth Immigration Act 1962'* [12,39] came into force limiting entry to legitimate full-time students, and persons with approved employment, who were capable of supporting themselves and their families. From 1st January 1973 holders of United Kingdom Citizenship *'were distinguished according to whether or not they had the right of abode in the United Kingdom'*. The *'British Nationality Act 1981'* abolished this single status and created three categories of citizenship namely *'British Citizen, British Dependent Territories Citizen, and British Overseas Citizen'*. A fourth national status was created with effect from 1st January 1987, the status of *'British National (Overseas)'*. Of these, only *British Citizenship* carries with it the right of abode in the United Kingdom. Holders of each of the other categories of citizenship, or national status are subject to immigration control. The establishment of British nationality status of *Anglo-Indians* in all cases is now decided initially from the Act extant when the person was born in India. For those born up to and including 31st December 1982 the Acts of 1948 and 1965 apply.[11,39] It has imposed considerable restrictions on *Anglo-Indians* from India, who in consequence looked more towards emigration to nations such as Australia and Canada, who they find more welcoming. In 1999 the British Government offered full *British Citizenship*, with right of abode in Great Britain, to the 130,000 remaining *British Dependent Territory Citizens*; residents of the last few surviving mostly island colonies of the once great British Empire, namely Anguilla, Bermuda, British Virgin Islands, Cayman Islands, Falkland Islands, Gibralter, Montserrat, Pitcairn, St. Helena, Ascension Island, Tristan da Cunha, Turks and Caicos Islands, British Antarctic Territory and British Indian Ocean Territory. They will be known as British Overseas Territories.

[NOTE: *The above is only my interpretation of the Acts. Persons should refer to the proper Immigration authorities for official confirmation*].

15. Post Raj Migration -

The British Indian Empire, as it was known, disappeared with the *India Independence Act 1947*. It was partitioned into India and Pakistan and both made independent precipitously by the British on 15th August 1947, with East Pakistan separating later to become Bangladesh in 1971 (see Part 2). Some basic political guarantees were provided for the *Anglo-Indian* Community, making it one of six politically recognised minorities in India. But fearing a loss of their identity and privileges enjoyed under the British *Raj*, and even their homes and livelihood, the majority of *Domiciled Europeans* and thousands of *Anglo-Indians* trapped in India, left before Independence, or soon after. Financial provision by way of 50 percent of sea passages to Britain, was allegedly made after Indian Independence by the British Government, for the evacuation of the British *Domiciled Europeans* and the *Anglo-Indians*, who could prove their British paternal origin. Those with a family member, either male or female, in the British or Indian services of His Majesties forces in India were dealt with more compassionately than those in civil occupations. Premature departees Home however in early 1947 had to find the whole cost of passage. My own father paid for the passages to England of my brother and myself in May 1947. Even skin colour was often waived aside. After all sun tans were common and desirable to many Europeans in the mid-1940's India, and proof of British ancestors after many generations in India was difficult. The former class were forced to find the remainder of the cost. All were faced with the enormous cost of kitting themselves out for the cold climate in *Blighty* and finding a home and a new job in Britain from their own resources, which in many cases took all their life's savings and reduced many to near poverty.[89] Many were older people, who stood little chance of obtaining employment elsewhere, feared their jobs were no longer guaranteed in India, as they had been with the British *Raj*. Most had no homes to return to in Britain or elsewhere. Their homes more often than not had been provided by the *Raj* in India. Many were children needing new schools and older ones in need of higher education, for which no grants were made readily available, as with British children living at Home, thus putting yet greater strain on the limited resources of their parents. Many families were broken up by these circumstances, and much grief and unhappiness resulted from the trauma of the time. Covenanted *Europeans* and *European* British troops in India were of course taken care of, and generous education grants provided for them and their children.

There were about 170,000 *Europeans* and 140,000 *Anglo-Indians* returned in the 1931 Census of India. That is a total for the combined communities of 310,000, out of a total population of about 400 million. Many argue that about 50,000 of those returned as *Europeans* were really fair *Anglo-Indians*, either masquerading as, or taken to be *Europeans* in error, or for political reasons. If true then there were only 120,000 *Europeans* and 190,000 *Anglo-Indians* in 1931. The largest concentration of *Anglo-Indians* in 1941 was in West Bengal, followed by the Madras Presidency, Bombay Presidency, United Provinces, Bihar and Central Provinces.[1] Only about 8,000 *Anglo-Indians* were reported to have ended up in Pakistan in 1947, of which only about a 1000 were in what was later to become Bangladesh.[2] About 25,000 *Anglo-Indians* made new lives for themselves in Australia, Canada and the United States of America, and many more made for Home, the hallowed memory of England, where their origins or race were not discriminated against officially, especially once they became assimilated.[61] Most were to become naturalised in the country of their adoption, where they became proud citizens of that country, and where their *Anglo-Indian* origins are no longer of official, nor social concern or consequence, except by their own choice.

The old *Anglo-Indian and Domiciled European Community* still like to keep in touch with each other in these countries, with the '*Anglo-Indian*

Association of Canada' in Mississagua, Ontario, the *'Australian Anglo-Indian Association'* in Perth, West Australia, and the *'Anglo-Indian Society of USA'* in Germantown, Maryland. In Britain, there is the **'British Ancestors in India Society'* (B.A.I.S.), (* now *British Ancestors in India (UK) Ltd*), 2 South Farm Avenue, Harthill, Sheffield S26 7WY, U.K. with its founder and editor Paul Rowland, which publishes the *'The Indiaman'* magazine, and the *'Anglo-Indian Family History Group'*, whose Founder and Editor Geraldine Charles 68 Greenway Close, Friern Barnet, London N11 3NT distributes *'The East Indies Telegraph'*. The *World Anglo-Indian Federation* has arranged *Anglo-Indian World Reunions* every three years throughout the Commonwealth, starting with England in 1989, Canada 1992, Australia in 1995 and Bangalore, India in 1998. The next one in 2001 is to be held in Auckland, New Zealand and the 2004 event in the U.S.A. The *Anglo-Indian (London) Social Club*, Hon.Sec. George Hillier, 944 Harrow Road,Sudbury, Wembley, Middlesex HA0 2PY arranges reunions, including the international reunion of which he is President. There are many thriving school Old Boys/Old Girls Associations, who meet annually to have a *buck;* see addresses in Hazel Craig's fine book *'Under the Old School Topee'* [17] (see Appendix 2).

The *Oriental & India Office Collections (O.I.O.C.)* of The British Library (B.L.), now at 96 Euston Road, St Pancras, London NW1 2DB and the Newspaper Library of B.L. at Collindale Ave., London NW9 5HE and the Public Record Office, Ruskin Ave., Kew, Richmond, Surrey TW9 4DU keep outstanding records of the British in India. The new *British Empire & Commonwealth Museum*, Clock Tower Yard, Temple Meads, Bristol BS1 6QH, U.K. displays much material and memorabilia of the *Raj*, and has oral records by old India hands. The small British India Museum, Newton St., Colne, Lancs. has some records and memorabilia also. The charity *British Association for Cemeteries in South Asia* (B.A.C.S.A.), Hon.Sec. Theon Wilkinson M.B.E., at 6.5 Chartfield Avenue, London SW15 6HQ concerns itself with the care of former British graves and cemeteries in south Asia and records monumental inscriptions. It also publishes a newsletter the *'Chowkidar'* and holds annual meetings in London. The *South India Association*, Hon.Sec Jane Turner, Monk's Hatch, Hogg's Back, Guildford, Surrey GU3 1DG also holds annual reunions in London. Cathie Campbell at 1/B Stonefield Place, Hawick, Roxburgshire, Scotland TD9 0EY is the Hon. Sec. for *Koi Hai Directory* and newsletter. The *Indian Army Association*, Hon. Sec. Lt.Col. Patric J. Emerson O.B.E., 20 Kings Road, Kingston upon Thames, Surrey, KT2 5HR have an annual newsletter. The *Women's Auxiliary Corps (India) W.A.C.(I) Association*, Hon.Sec. Joan Collins, 85 Valleyfields Road, London SW16 2HX hold an annual reunion in London. The *British Commonwealth Ex-Services League*, Secretary General Lt.Col.S. Pope O.B.E., R.M., 48 Pall Mall, London SW1Y 5JG monitor the needs of Commonwealth ex-servicemen. *Families in British India Society* (F.I.B.I.S.), Hon.Sec. Tony Fuller, 81 Rosewood Ave, Elm Park, Hornchurch, Essex RM12 5LD, produces a useful family history journal. Cathy Day's (Australia) Family History in India internet web site: *www.ozemail.com.au/~clday* is excellent on family history research in India and India Mailing List (e-mail: *INDIA-L@rootsweb.com*) is an excellent source. Dr.Adrian Gilbert's (Australia) *Anglo-Indian* web site *www.alphalink.com.au/~agilbert/index* and

Withbert Payne's (U.S.A.) *Anglo-Indians* web site: *www. anglo-indians.com* are also very worth accessing.

16. Staying On -

Most *Europeans* and *Anglo-Indians* who stayed behind continue to do well in all spheres of activity and greatly contribute to the non-discriminatory secular state that India has become, but there are also many exceptions. The number of *Anglo-Indians* remaining behind *'according to 1951 census was 111,637.'* V.R.Gaikwad in his book *'The Anglo-Indians'* [32] found from a sample survey he did in the 1960's of *Anglo-Indians* who 'stayed behind' in India, that in three typical towns of Bangalore, Jhansi and Bilaspur, about 41% thought they would be happier in the United Kingdom, 1.5% in Australia, 9.3% in New Zealand, 10.8% in India and 9.3% in other countries. The remainder were undecided.

By the Indian Constitution, which took effect from January 1951, *Anglo-Indians* who chose to remain in India after Independence in 1947, were recognised as a distinct minority community in independent India, and were given safeguards by way of the right of representation in the provincial and national government. They were given special provisions for education and for services in the Railways, Customs and Excise and Post and Telegraphs for a period of 10 years, to permit the community *'to find its feet in the new India, politically, economically, socially, culturally and psychologically.'* Furthermore they were welcome to apply for any level of the civil or military service, and have held many senior posts in the Indian, Pakistani and Bangladeshi Army, Navy and Air Force since. In the post *Raj* Kashmir campaign two-thirds of the pilots decorated for gallantry were *Anglo-Indians*. Jack Mungavin, who was Head Boy of Barnes High School, Deolali, when I was there, became Rear Admiral of the Pakistan Navy. Frank Anthony, a country-born lawyer, who succeeded Sir Henry Gidney as the leader of the *Anglo-Indian* Community, and President of the *'All India Anglo-Indian Association'* in 1942, and became a Member of the Indian *Lok Sabha* (Parliament), has aggressively pursued the interests of the *Anglo-Indian Community* since Independence, as fully recognised Indian nationals. He also established their native language, English, as an official language of the government and their separate *Anglo-Indian* culture as an officially recognised ethnic minority, especially as they are now in open competition with indigenous Indians, in employment and society generally. He has ensured that the *Anglo-Indian* schools continue with their excellent education and in English, although the numbers of Indians otherwise attending them have greatly increased in number, and has himself inaugurated a plan for 20 new *Anglo-Indian* schools all over India, called Frank Anthony schools. These are independently financed, to ensure that the *Anglo-Indian* culture survives[1,2] (see Appendix 2). Major General Robert G. Williams succeeded Frank Anthony as President of the *'Anglo-Indian Association'* in 1993 when the former died.[17] I understand General Williams passed away in 1999 and was succeeded by Neil O'Brien from Calcutta.

17. Achievement -

The great success of British *Europeans* is well recorded in history (see Part 2). However, with some spectacular exceptions, relatively less reference is made to the *Anglo-Indian and Domiciled European Community*, without whom history may not have been made. Some *Domiciled Europeans* in India stayed faithful to their kind. Others married into wealthy and princely Indian families, or resorted to more modest liaisons with local girls. Both the *Domiciled Europeans* and their children whether of mixed marriages, the *Anglo-Indians*, or not, did achieve great fame, or notoriety in India, and at Home in Great Britain, before and during the British *Raj*. Many more became very successful professionally and in military careers in Britain, U.S.A., and the Commonwealth countries of Canada, Australia and South Africa, when they left India after Independence from the *Raj* in 1947. Many that stayed behind did so in India, Pakistan and Bangladesh. The more publicised of these, during the early years of the *Raj*, included many military adventurers or freelances, or what has become known as mercenaries in modern parlance. They offered their services as officers in the armies of native *Maharajahs* and *Maratha* waring chiefs, like the *Peshwa* at Poona, Scindhia at Gwalior, Holkar at Indore and Bhonsla at Nagpur, whose main interest after territorial gain was plunder. Whilst the more honourable of these mercenaries deserted, rather than engage in battle with their own kith and kin in the British Army, most did not shy from direct confrontation with their brother *European* officers in opposing native armies. Some were discharged, or summarily executed by the Indian chiefs they served, or their military Generals, who were also often *European*, when desertion or treachery was suspected, when combating the British. These included Colonel Vickers, and his companions Ryan and Dodd who were beheaded in 1803 by the *Maratha* Chieftain Holkar. A great number of these freelances were French, formerly part of the original French army defeated by General Lord Robert Clive of the Company's British Army, and other *Europeans*. Many of these freelances, from whatever origin, were subsequently persuaded to join the British forces, on an irregular basis, often on pain of death, if found bearing arms for an enemy.

Foremost of the British soldiers was Colonel James Skinner, known fondly by the Indians as '*Sikander Sahib*' (after Alexander the Great), who founded the famous Skinner's Irregular Horse cavalry regiment, the Yellow Boys, in 1803. Skinner's Horse was up to 3000 strong when he joined the British Army under General Lord Lake, who already had some 20,000 cavalry in his campaign against the *Marathas*, after having first served with the *Maratha* Chief Mahdaji Scindhia. The regiment continued in India as Skinner's Horse (1st Duke of York's Own Cavalry). He was the son of Scottish Lieutenant Colonel Hercules Skinner, of the British Army and the daughter of a captured Rajput *zamindar* (land-owner). He had estates near Delhi at Belaspur, Muttra and Hansi, where he lived with his *Muslim bibi* (wife) and *harem* and left many progeny, some of whom followed their colourful ancestor into Skinner's Horse. He was the author of two books on the princes and people of India and received from the Indian *Moghul* Emperor the exotic title of '*Nasir-ud-Dowlah* Colonel James Skinner

Bahadur Ghalib Jang' (Most Exalted, Victorious in War). He built the first proper Christian Church of St James in Delhi in 1836. [47]

Another was Irishman, Colonel William Linnaeus Gardner, the nephew of the first Lord Gardner of Uttoxeter, who first fought with the *Maratha* Chief Holkar and the *Maharajah* of Jaipur, before raising Gardner's Irregular Horse for the British Army commanded by General Lord Lake in 1809. He was married to the grand-daughter of the *Nawab* of Cambay, the adopted daughter of the *Moghul* Emperor, and had a large estate granted to his wife by the Indian Emperor, at Khasgunge, in northern India. He is alleged to have descendants who may be eligible to claim the vacant English barony of his uncle.[78] The Gardners form a numerous family of *Anglo-Indians* in India, although only James Gardner followed his father into Gardner's Horse. Equally opportunistic as a mercenary at that time was William Gardner's brother-in-law Major Hyder Young Hearsey, who married another grand-daughter of the *Nawab* of Cambay. His English cousin General Sir John Hearsey, one of the many British heroes of the Indian Mutiny of 1857, married a daughter of his and their descendants continued to serve in Gardner's Horse, now known as the 2nd Lancers (Gardner's Horse).[70] The House of the Earl of Duffus, in Scotland also has *Anglo-Indian* descendants who pride in the name of Sutherland.[2] A Scotsman Colonel Robert Sutherland, cashiered from the Royal Highland Regiment of the British Army, was a well known freelance soldier, who served in the *Maratha* Chief Madhaji Scindhia's army in the early 1800's, and had native wives and children.

Another colourful adventurer of the time was the Irish *Rajah* George Thomas, a deserter from a British man-of-war at Madras and known throughout India as 'War*like George*', who carved out a 3000 square mile kingdom for himself in Hariana near Delhi and raised a large and proficient private army. He ruled benevolently from his capital at Hansi, where he had a large *harem* and numerous children, until defeated and ejected by the army of the *Maratha* Chief Mahdaji Scindhia, whom he had often fought for, in 1802, as the *Marathas* feared his successes in the Punjab were thwarting their own territorial ambitions.[44]

Amongst the civilians, Englishman Job Charnock, who founded Calcutta in 17th century, was married to a *Hindu* women he saved from her husband's funeral pyre. His daughter married Irishman Sir Eyre Coote, who fought at the Battle of Plassey with Lord Robert Clive in 1757 and followed him as the Commander in Chief of the British Army in India. There were also many other *European* mercenaries during the late Eighteenth and early Nineteenth centuries, who also had children of Indian wives. Two of the more publicised Lieutenant Benoit de Boigne and Sergeant-Major Pierre Cullier Perron, once of the French Army, were in turn to become Commander-in-Chief of the *Maratha* Chief Mahdaji Scindhia's army and Governor of *Hindustan*. The former who ended up a very wealthy man, was granted the honourable title of Count de Boigne by no less a person than Napoleon Bonaparte, the French Emperor, on his eventual return to France.[6]

The illustrious Field Marshal Earl Roberts of Kandahar, Pretoria and Waterford, known fondly as 'Bobs', was immortalised by Rudyard Kipling, and won the Victoria Cross in the Indian Mutiny of 1857. He was Assistant Quartermaster General in the Abyssinia campaign in 1868, distinguished himself in the Afghan Wars in the 1870's, was Commander in Chief of British Army in India in 1885, in Ireland in 1895 and in the Boer Wars in South Africa in 1901, and the last Supreme Commander of all British Land Forces world wide the same year. He was born in Cawnpore (*Kanpur*), and was said to be the grandson of a *Rajput* princess who was married to a Colonel Kennedy.[41,75] Even the maternal grandmother of Lord Liverpool, Tory Prime Minister of Great Britain in 1812, was said to be a Calcutta woman.[63] Baron Charles Metcalfe, who was British Resident in Delhi in 1811 and Lieutenant Governor of the North West Frontier Province in 1837, had three sons by an Indian wife.[28] General Sir David Ochterlony, the colourful British Resident in Delhi in 1821, lived in the style of an Indian *Rajah* and is said to have had 13 Indian 'wives'.[28] Earlier in 1805 Scotsman William Fraser was said to have fathered many children from his harem of wives in Delhi.[19] Brigadier-General Reginald Dyer the British Officer responsible for what became known as the Armritsar Massacre in 1919, was born in India.[49] Others were Sir Hugh Massy Wheeler of Mutiny fame and James Kyd, the Master Shipbuilder to the East India Company. Also William Palmer, who founded the great banking house of Palmer & Co at Hyderabad in 1814. His father, another William Palmer was military secretary to Warren Hastings, and was descended on the maternal side from *Rani* Faiz Bakhsh, who was related to the ruling *Moghul* families of Lucknow and Delhi.[1,62]

Frank Anthony, in his book *'Britain's Betrayal in India'*[2] vividly describes the achievement of many *Anglo-Indians* during both World Wars in all arms of the service, including the award of many Victoria Crosses (V.C.), for conspicuous bravery. These include Flight Lieutenant Lief Robinson of the R.A.F. in World War 1, who shot down the first Zeppelin over England. Also, in World War 2, the courageous Wing Commander Guy Gibson V.C., of the R.A.F., who was born in Simla, hero of the dangerous bombing of the German Mohne and Eder dams in Germany, successfully disabling the armaments manufacturing capacity of the Ruhr. Also Major Frank G. Blaker, of 3/9th Gurkha Rifles in Burma, who also won the Military Cross there. Captain N.J.M. 'Ginger' Pettengell from Jubbulpore won the Military Cross (M.C.) fighting in Africa and Italy. His cousin Edgar Pettengell became a Major-General in the Indian Army in the 1960's. Major John Hartley won an M.C. in Italy. Major Betrand Litchfield won an M.C. in Burma, as did Major Reginald Noronha, Brigadier George Jenkins, Captain William Lopez (I.M.S.). Dr. George Rodriques G.C. of the Indian Medical Service (I.M.D.) British Cadre, was mentioned in several dispatches in the Great War in Mesopotamia and France, and was recommended for the Military Cross during the Arab Rebellion in 1920. Following an operation with the Dorset Regiment in Malabar in 1921 he was awarded the Order of the British Empire (O.B.E.) Military Division, for gallantry during the Moplah Rebellion. In 1942 he was awarded the George Cross (G.C.) in place of his O.B.E. Helen Rodriques G.M., matron of the Civil Hospital, Taunggyi was awarded the George Medal (G.M.) for *'utmost courage and devotion to duty'* during Japanese bombing raids on the hospital.[2]

The popular author John Masters' autobiographical experiences in the Indian Army give a vivid description of his part of the war against the Japanese in Burma in 1941 - 1945 in *'The Road Past Mandalay'* [58], and his earlier army experiences in *'Bugles and the Tiger'* [57] is used as a text book for young officer recruits in the service. His highly successful fictional novel *'Bhowani Junction'*[56] and film, first gave world-wide modern media exposure (albeit in an unflattering way) to the *Anglo-Indian* Community in India during World War 2. He was a fifth generation *Anglo-Indian* himself, born in Calcutta. He was second in command to General Rees in the *Chindits* at the defeat of the Japanese at the battle for Mandalay in 1945.[58] (see Part 2). His great, great, great grandfather Scotsman William Stuart, whilst an officer in *Maharajah* Scindhia's army during the *Maratha* War in 1785, married an Indian *Muslim* from Delhi. Their granddaughter married William Masters, John Masters' great grandfather, who was the first Headmaster of the Parental Academy, in Calcutta in 1823, one of the earliest *Anglo-Indian* schools in India, the Verulam's Academy in 1828, and the still famous La Martinière College, Calcutta in 1836. His paternal great great grandfather William Masters, first went out to India in 1804, from Wiltshire, in the King's Royal Irish Light Dragoons.[16]

General Sir Michael Rose, the Commander of the crack British Special Air Service (S.A.S.) and the Commander of the United Nations Protection Force (UNPROFOR) in Bosnia during the civil war there in 1996, one of the most decorated and experienced British battle commanders, and the step son of John Masters, was born in Quetta. (The *Sunday Telegraph* 12 January 1997).

Many *Anglo-Indians* and *Domiciled Europeans* in the Indian Medical Department (I.M.D.) had brilliant careers both in the service and in private medicine subsequently. The precursors were the Apothecaries of the British Army. Among these were Sir Patrick Hehir, K.C.I.E., K.C.B., Sir John Tytler, Col. Mulrowny, Col. Sykes, Col. O'Gorman and Sir Henry Gidney. [2]

Amongst successful western entertainment celebrities are British Citizens Sir Cliff Richard (real name Harry Webb), who was born in Lucknow,[2,62,89] Englebert Humperdinck (real name Arnold George Dorsey, but sometimes referred to as Jerry Dorsey) was born in Madras,[2,62] and Tony Brent (real name Reginald Bretagne) who was born in Bombay. [2,62] Cliff Richard was knighted by Queen Elizabeth II of England in June 1995, for his services to entertainment and his considerable work and contributions to charities. He chose to retain his performing pseudonym for the honour, and is known as Sir Cliff Richard. Glamourous film star of the 1940's and 1950's Merle Oberon, later Lady Korda, the wife of film director Sir Alexander Korda, started life as a typist for Burmah Shell in Calcutta. Terence Alan Milligan, the hilariously funny and extremely successful Irish radio and television comedian, author and poet known as 'Spike' Milligan, was born in Ahmednagar, the son of a Bombadier in the

Royal Horse Artillery.[59] His grandmother and mine were friends and neighbours in the Military Widows Quarters in Poona. Eminent Radio and Television Journalist Mark Tully, once Chief of the British Broadcasting Corporation Bureau in New Delhi, and popular India correspondent in the 1970's, 1980's and 1990's, and author of several good books about India and Indian life, was born in Calcutta. He was awarded the *Padma Shri* by the President of India, in 1992, and was also decorated with the O.B.E. by the monarch of Great Britain, Queen Elizabeth II. The supreme actor Ben Kingsley who played a stirring part as the much revered Indian visionary Mahatma Gandhi, immortalised in Richard Attenborough's production of the film '*Gandhi*', was described as '*part-Indian*' in the *Daily Telegraph* newspaper of 30th January 1998, the anniversary of Gandhi's death. A 19th century poet named Henry Vivian Derozio, whose poetry and teaching sprang from a deep love for India, and who has been compared with the renowned Indian poet Rabindranath Tagore, was a very well known and socially active *Anglo-Indian*.[26,71]

There were and still are many accomplished *Anglo-Indian* sportsmen and sports women, especially in hockey and athletics, with some men representing India in most Olympiads. The bulk of the Indian international hockey teams until partition in India consisted of *Anglo-Indians*. India won the mens Olympic Games hockey in 1928 and 1948 and has always been in the top handful of teams in the world. Their teams were successful in the majority of premier tournaments in Indian national tournaments during the *Raj*, including the men's Calcutta Hockey League and the Aga Khan Tournament in Bombay.

Hundreds of Christian Missionaries of every denomination played an important part in the social reform of India, although initially both the East India Company and the Indian religious leaders were concerned about their religious intentions, until about 1835. They included many *Domiciled European* and *Anglo-Indians*. Their mission schools, colleges, orphanages and hospitals are a byword amongst the *Anglo-Indian* and Indian Communities (see Appendix 2).

The supreme *European* domiciled in India, who took Indian citizenship, must surely be the blessed Mother Teresa, the Albanian born former Loretto nun and head of the Missionaries of Charity she formed in Calcutta in 1950. She cared for '*the poorest of the poor*' in Calcutta first, by providing a home for the destitute and dying off the streets. Her Missionaries of Charity, with their children's homes and hospitals for the destitute, can now be found in over a hundred countries all over the world, caring for the needy. She was awarded the Pope John XXIII Peace Prize by Pope Paul VI in 1971 and the Nobel Peace Prize in 1979, for her work so eloquently described by Malcolm Muggeridge in '*Something Beautiful for God*'[65] She sadly died in India in 1997 and was given a full State Funeral by the Indian Government, attended by senior representatives from around the world. *Hindus, Muslims* and Christians alike considered her a Saint, and after her death there was talk of formalising this.

Also amongst the *European* missionary doctors domiciled in India was the revered figure of Sir Henry Holland, of the Church Missionary Society, the eminent eye surgeon, whose name was a household word in the North West Frontier of India from 1900, especially in Baluchistan and the Sind, in Quetta, Shikarpur and Jacobabad, in present day Pakistan. He was succeeded after his retirement in 1948 by his equally revered sons Dr.Harry and Dr. Ronnie Holland who had been working with him since 1935 and 1940 respectively, and whom I had the pleasure of once meeting in Quetta in 1963. Many thousands of Indians and Pakistanis have been given a new lease of life following cataract operations carried out on their sightless eyes, at these Christian Missionary hospitals which are still operating to this day, so vividly described in Sir Henry's book *'Frontier Doctor'*.[46]

The first nurses assisting in the Missionary and other British hospitals were young *Anglo-Indian* and *Domiciled European* women, as the rigid caste systems of India forbad their women from taking part publicly in these activities at that time. Their services were also in great demand in the administrative offices of the *Raj* as stenographers and secretaries.

Speaking at the centenary celebrations in 1976 of the *'Anglo-Indian Association in India'*, the Indian Prime Minister, the late Indira Gandhi, paid the following tribute to the *Anglo-Indian Community* in India;-

> *'The Anglo-Indian Community has been a pioneer in many technical professions: railways and aviation, forestry, in education, public life, nursing and sport and in our fighting forces. The entire country admires their zest, their spirit of adventure and their patriotism.'*[1]

However 50 years after Indian Independence in 1947 the *Anglo-Indian Community* in India, which now only numbers about 100,000 nationwide, is said, according to Louise Fraser in the Newcastle Morning Herald in Australia on 7th June 1994, *' to be in serious trouble, considered by many to be worse off than the lowest Hindu caste.'* The majority of *Anglo - Indians* in southern India in particular were said to be unemployed, and the majority of their children lack proper education.

PART 2

BRITISH RAJ INDIA HISTORY

Take up the white man's burden-
Send forth the best ye breed -
Go bind your sons to exile
To serve your captives' need;

('*The White Man's Burden*' by Rudyard Kipling 1899)

1. First 100 Years 1600 - 1700 -

BRITISH INTEREST AND INFLUENCE in India stretched over a period of nearly 350 years. Amongst the earliest British *Europeans* of note in India were many whose names were familiar to later residents, both native and *European*. Their legendary fame arose from their exploits and achievements. Important structures, bridges, roads, irrigation barrages, administrative buildings towns and cantonments, were named after them during the British *Raj*, or *Sirkar* (government - the British Indian Government) - names like Curzon Street, Elphinstone Street, Napier Road, Lloyd Barrage and the town of Jacobabad. It is comical to relate that although after Indian Independence in 1947 the Indians changed many English names to somewhat longer Indian ones, in their desire to remove all trace of the supposedly hated British, the original English names are still more familiar to taxi drivers, and local people, especially those of the older generation.

In AD 1600 Queen Elizabeth I of England and Ireland (1558 - 1603), granted the Honourable East India Company (E.I.C.) a Royal Charter to trade in India, during the reign of the greatest of Indian monarchs, the Emperor Akbar the Great (1556 - 1605), who is commonly credited with having founded the Indian *Moghul* Empire. Although a *Muslim*, he was commendably tolerant of the many other religions of the 100 million people of the land, most of which predated *Islam* (founded c.610 AD), such as *Hinduism* (founded c.2000 to 1000 BC), *Jainism* (c.540 BC), *Buddhism* (c.527 BC), *Sikhism* (c.1500 AD), the many varieties of Christianity (c.30 AD). In 1591 an English adventurer named Ralph Fitch, returned to England from his travels in India, with lavish tales of trading opportunities. At that time the Dutch had a monopoly in the trade of the exotic spices (pepper and condiments) from the spice islands of the East Indies.These had become an

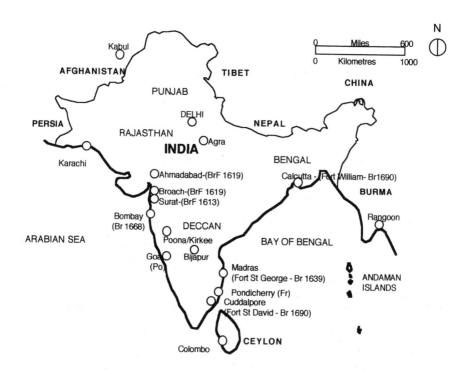

N

| | Miles | 600 |
| 0 | Kilometres | 1000 |

Kabul

AFGHANISTAN   TIBET

CHINA

PUNJAB

PERSIA

DELHI

NEPAL

RAJASTHAN

INDIA Agra

Karachi

BENGAL

Ahmadabad-(BrF 1619)

Calcutta - Fort William- Br1690)

Broach-(BrF 1619)

Surat-(BrF 1613)

BURMA

Bombay
(Br 1668)

DECCAN

Rangoon

ARABIAN SEA

Poona/Kirkee

Goa   Bijapur
(Po)

BAY OF BENGAL

Madras
(Fort St George - Br 1639)

ANDAMAN
ISLANDS

Pondicherry (Fr)
Cuddalpore
(Fort St David - Br 1690)

Colombo

CEYLON

Figure 1 -
BRITISH INDIA - FIRST 100 YEARS, 1600 TO 1700

Note: Br = British town : BrF = British Factory only
Fr = French town : Po = Portuguese town

exciting, addictive, and very profitable gourmet supplement to dull English fare. Then it was only affordable by the wealthy. But now they are enjoyed by all, especially in the form of delicious curries retailed by the many Indian and other oriental restaurants. These two conjoining circumstances were the joint trigger for the launching of *'the worshipful company of London merchants trading in the East Indies'*. Following an unsuccessful contretemps with the belligerent Dutch in the East Indies, the E.I.C. fortuitously discovered spices in south India also, where the friendly and co-operative *Sultan* of Bijapur was the Indian peninsula representative of the *Moghul* Emperor.[75] The occupation of India subsequently became almost inevitable.

Captain William Hawkins, Sir Henry Middleton, Thomas Best and Sir Thomas Roe, the first British Ambassadors to the court of the *Moghul* Emperor in Delhi, were instrumental in defeating the opposition of the Portuguese, the first *European* traders in India, to the British legitimate trading interests in the sub-continent. They persuaded the Emperor Jahangir (1605 -1627) to permit the first British trading settlement (known as a factory) with associated fortifications at Surat on the north-west coast of the Indian Deccan peninsula in 1613, followed by others at Agra, Ahmedabad and Broach in 1619, during the reign of King James I of England (1603 -1625).

In the reign of King Charles I of England (1625 - 1649), and the *Moghul* Emperor Shah Jehan (1627 - 1658), builder of the world famous and beautiful Taj Mahal in Agra, the city of Madras *(Chennai)* (Fort Saint George) was founded on the east coast of India by the Englishman Francis Day, of the E.I.C. in 1639. It became the fourth largest town in India, and capital and seat of the Governor of the Madras Presidency, during the British *Raj*. During the reign of, what has been described as the last great Indian Emperor, Aurangzeb (1658 - 1707), the British founded the great city of Bombay (*Mumbai*), which became the capital of and seat of the British Governor of the Bombay Presidency. It was first acquired as a single island off the west coast of India, by the English King Charles II (1660 - 1685), from his marriage to the Portuguese Princess Catherine of Braganza in 1661, as part of her dowry. The King rented it to the E.I.C. in 1668 for £10 a year. Subsequently six further islands were added. These were connected following huge reclamation works, providing a magnificent natural harbour. With the advent of the Suez Canal in Egypt in 1869 and the railways in India after 1853, Bombay expanded to become a very successful commercial city and seaport, and one of the four major cities of India. After Independence in 1947, it also became the most populous. It was named after the goddess of the local *Koli* people *Mumbadevi*, or *Mumbai*, supposedly corrupted by the British to *Bom Bhia* ('beautiful bay'), and hence Bombay. Bombay was established by the British Governor Gerald Aungier of Surat. He also formed the first *European* army regiment in India, the Bombay (*European*) Fusiliers, of the E.I.C. in 1662. Bombay soon supplanted Surat as the west coast headquarters of the E.I.C. in 1687. After false starts at Cuttack (1633), Hoogly (1651) and Chittagong (1689), Englishman Job Charnock of the E.I.C. laid the foundations for Fort William, (Calcutta, now *Kolkata*) in Bengal in 1690, in the reign of King William III and Queen

Mary of England and Ireland (1689 - 1702). Englishman Sir Charles Eyre became the President and first Governor. Calcutta, which was located on the banks of the navigable River Hoogly, was to become the first capital of British India, and remained such until 1911, when it moved to New Delhi, the new town built by the British outside the old *Moghul* capital of Delhi. It was at one time the largest city in India, and the greatest commercial and cultural centre in Asia. It was named after *Kalikata*, one of three villages existing in the area, which was itself named after *Kali*, the most fearsome goddess in the *Hindu* pantheon of deities (see Figure 1).

The religious persecution of the *Hindu* majority in India, during the bigoted *Muslim* fundamentalist reign of the *Moghul* Emperor Aurangzeb, and the 50 percent of agricultural produce land tax he imposed generally, started the great revolt amongst the *Hindu Rajputs* of Rajasthan, the *Jats* and *Sikhs* of the Punjab in north of India, and the *Hindu Marathas*, in the *Deccan*. The collapse of the great *Moghul* Empire which followed led to the anarchy and chaos that the British were forced to control to protect their trading interests. The Indian *Moghul* Emperors that followed Aurangzeb were inept and otherwise puppets of powerful courtiers, or warring factions in the sub-continent.

Chatrapati Shivaji, known as 'the Grand Rebel' to the English and 'the Mountain Rat' to the *Moghul* Emperor Aurangzeb, was a swashbuckling *Hindu Maratha* Chieftain, whose courage and audacity against the all powerful forces of the dominant *Moghul Muslim Raj* of the time, gave him fame, fortune and a kingdom in the modern day Maharashtra, where he is greatly revered. Poona (*Pune*), a town which achieved fame in Britain as the source of classical Victorian yarns about the old *Anglo-Indian* military (especially colonel *sahibs*), was then the chief town of Shivaji's terrain, although he then operated out of the nearby fortress at Raigad, a ruin today. Poona was known then only for its temples and the orthodoxy of its *Hindu* priests, a precursor to its religious *ashrams* of modern times, which are internationally renowned. Shivaji first came up against the fledgling English presence in India, when he captured and imprisoned four of the Company's factors for 'gun running' to an enemy neighbour, the *Muslim Nawab* of Bijapur, in 1660. But soon after, the English, who were impressed by Shivaji's fighting qualities, were supplying him not only with artillery, but gunners as well. In 1670 he attacked Surat a second time with an army of 15,000, and although his prime aim was to bloody the nose of the *Moghuls*, he sought also to procure loot from the many wealthy international traders there, which included the English. However, whereas the rest suffered, the English stood their ground against him, successfully protecting their factory. By 1674 Shivaji was supreme in Southern India and crowned himself King of *Hindu* India. During a preliminary ceremony whilst Shivaji was in prayer to the Mother Goddess at Pratapgad, he fell into a trance. A voice from within him prophesied the final collapse of the *Moghul* Empire, and the entry of the *Marathas* into Delhi and also that *'The sceptre shall pass into the hands of a strange people with red faces'*. [49] (No one will doubt that the Englishman's face does get very red in the tropical heat of India). Shivaji also had a powerful navy, with which he engaged in trading with Persia, Iraq and Arabia, and which he used in the movement of his troops in battle. It was also used to harass *Moghul* trading ships and ship-loads of *Muslim* pilgrims on their way to Mecca. On an occasion in 1679 he engaged the English ships successfully when he landed at Khanderi, near Bombay (see Fig. 1).

2. Second 100 Years 1700 - 1800 -

During the reigns of Queen Anne (1702 - 1714), King George I (1714 - 1727) and George II of Great Britain and Ireland (1727 - 1760) the British were engaged in overcoming in the main the territorial ambitions of the French, under the Frenchman Robert Dupleix, Governor of Pondicherry. They had become the dominant foreign trading power in India after successfully withstanding rebellious native forces during the firm but short reign of Emperor Bahadur Shah (1707-1712). In the three huge trading and administrative regions of the E.I.C., known as the Bengal, Bombay and Madras Presidencies, the company had its own army to protect its trade and keep order (see Fig. 6). The army was manned almost entirely by Indian soldiers, with Indian officers also. After the destruction of Madras (Fort St. George) by the French, Cuddalpore (Fort St. David) further down the coast became the headquarters of Madras Presidency. Orders were given for all British forts in India to be strengthened, on the advice of perhaps the first qualified Civil Engineer in India, who was elected Engineer-General to the E.I.C. in 1749. His name was Benjamin Robins, a cheerful, unpretentious Quaker, and Fellow of the Royal Society (F.R.S.) in 1727 at 21 years old, who was a scientific contemporary of renowned Sir Isaac Newton. By 1751 he died of fever and overwork. He was succeeded by James Brohier. [76]

In 1748 the three far flung armies of the E.I.C.were placed under one Commander-in-Chief named Major Stringer Lawrence, regarded as being 'the father of the Indian Army'. The original small garrisons of Company native *sepoys* (originated from Persian *'sipah'* or army) were first supplemented by King's Troops in 1748. The forces were aided by Commodore Curtis Barnett and Admiral Edward Boscawen at sea. [33] The Englishman Robert Clive, later to become the Irish peer Lord Clive of Plassey, and known as the 'founder of the British *Raj'*, had a great victory against the French at the battle of Arcot in 1751. He became Commander-in-Chief in 1756 and reorganised the Indian Army on the lines of the British Army, introducing *European* officers to the senior posts. In 1757 he defeated the powerful Indian *Nawab* of Bengal Siraj-ud-daula and his French allies, in an extraordinary victory at Plassey, thus reversing the humiliation of the infamous and brutal castigation of 146 British *Europeans* in a 20 foot square suffocating prison cell in Fort William until their death in 1756, in what became known as 'the Black Hole of Calcutta'. Clive had only 3000 troops, a third of which were *Europeans*, against 50,000 of the enemy, but with *European* officers. From this victory the Company acquired control of the province of Bengal. In gratitude Clive was made Governor of the Company's possessions in Bengal (1758-1760 & 1765-1767). Anglo-Irishman Sir Eyre Coote defeated the French again at Wandiwash in 1760 and captured Pondicherry, the last

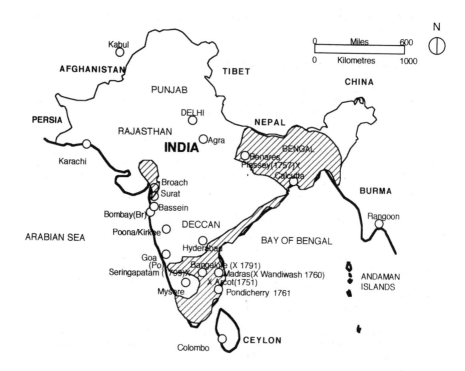

Figure 2 -
BRITISH INDIA - SECOND 100 YEARS, 1700 TO 1800

Note: Br = British town
    Fr = French town : Po = Portuguese town
    X = Battle
    ▨ = British Territory by 1800

main French bastion in India, in 1761. During the Seven Years War with France, which had spread to India, Great Britain had succeeded in becoming the major *European* power in India [13,33,57,78] (see Fig.2).

During the reign of British King George III (1760 - 1820), Englishman Warren Hastings, was the first and most famous Governor-General of the British possessions in India (1774 - 1785), after having first followed Clive as Governor of Bengal (1772-1774). After his resignation in 1784 he was impeached for alleged governmental irregularities by an ungrateful British Parliament, and although acquitted, was financially ruined. He laid the foundations of the Indian Civil Service (I.C.S.) and established the Supreme Court in Calcutta, under a Regulating Act 1773, in the words of Edmund Burke '*to form a strong and solid security for the natives against the wrongs and oppressions of British subjects resident in Bengal*'.[23] He was also successful in directing the confrontation of the Chiefs of the *Maratha* Confederacy, and the Nizam of Hyderabad in the Deccan (1774 - 1778). During the Premiership in Britain of William Pitt, the *India Act of 1784* dictated that the E.I.C. was in future to be responsible for the welfare of the people it governed. Furthermore a Parliamentary Board of Control was elected to scrutinise the affairs of the E.I.C., and select all future Governor-Generals from persons outside the Company. Irishman Charles Marquess Cornwallis, the next Governor General and Commander-in-Chief (1786 - 1793), was the first nobleman to rule India. He defeated the infamous Tippoo Sultan, 'Tiger of Mysore', in the 1st Mysore War at Bangalore in 1791, and reduced the French settlement at Pondicherry. In the rule of Sir John Shore, Baron Teignmouth (1793 - 1798), nothing of significance took place, except that in 1795, largely due to the efforts of Jonathan Duncan, the Company's Resident at Benares, female infanticide, (the deliberate killing by their parents of economically undesirable girl babies), was declared murder, but was difficult to enforce. In 1797 Tippoo Sultan and a French mercenary, Francis de Raymond had invited the Emperor of France, Napoleon Bonaparte to invade India and defeat the British whilst he was campaigning in Egypt. This was however foiled by the English Admiral Lord Horatio Nelson's victory against him at Aboukir, near Alexandria, at the mouth of the River Nile in Egypt in 1798 (see Fig. 2).

3. Third 100 Years - (a) 1800 to the Indian Mutiny of 1857

The Irish peer Richard Marquess Wellesley, Earl of Mornington, who followed as Governor-General (1798 to 1805), together with his brother General Arthur Wellesley (later to become the famed Duke of Wellington), and also the English Commander-in-Chief General (later Viscount) Gerard Lake, subdued the remainder of the Deccan and central India, a vast area of the sub-continent extending from Mysore to Delhi. Tippoo Sultan was defeated and killed at Seringapatam (1799) in the 2nd Mysore War, resulting in British rule in Mysore. British prominence in the Kingdom of Oudh at Lucknow was confirmed in 1801. The *Maratha* Confederacy was also reduced with the 1st and 2nd *Maratha* Wars, in which the *Maratha* Chief Scindhia was defeated at Delhi and Agra in 1803. The Indian Emperor Shah Alam II,

Figure 3:
BRITISH RAJ INDIA - THE MARATHA WARS 1800 - 1819

Note: Br = British town
  Fr = French town : Po = Portuguese town
  X = Battle
  ⧄ = British Territory by 1800

who had been under the protection of the *Marathas*, was rescued and placed under British protection instead. The same year the *Peshwa*, the *Maratha* Confederacy Chief Minister, Bhaji Rao II, acquiesced to the British by the Treaty of Bassein and Poona was occupied by Wellesley. The rebel *Maratha* Chiefs Scindhia, Holkar and Bhonsla were pursued and defeated in 1804 at the famous battle of Assaye, and ultimately at Ahmednagar and Argaum (see Fig. 3). [5,57,81] At this time the Presidency armies were further increased to a 154,000 British and Indian troops.[54] A possible ancestor of mine, a Sergeant in the 1st/4th Regiment from Bombay, was engaged in the battle of Assaye with General Wellesley.

In 1805 Lord Cornwallis returned to India to become Governor-General for a second time, and was succeeded by Scotsman Gilbert Elliot, Earl of Minto (1807 - 1813). The *India Act 1813* ended the E.I.C. monopoly of trade, opening its territories to British commerce and to Christian preaching.[76] The Anglican Bishopric of Calcutta was created that year. In 1822 the diocese extended to the whole of India, when Reginald Heber was the Bishop. Then followed the Irish Earl of Moira, Francis Rawdon, later Marquess of Hastings (unrelated to Warren Hastings), as Governor-General (1814 - 1823). He was aided by the Scottish Lord Mountstuart Elphinstone, British Political Resident at Poona (1811) and later Governor of Bombay (1819 - 1827), the Scottish General Sir John Malcolm, Lord Charles Metcalfe, Sir Thomas Munro and Generals Sir David Ochterlony, Sir Thomas Hislop and John Doveton. Mutinies in the Madras Army in Vellore in 1807, when British officers and men were massacred, and in the Bengal Army in Barrackpore in 1824 were brought under control. They suppressed the *Gurkhas* of Nepal (1816), who subsequently entered the Indian and British Armies, to form some of the finest fighting men in the world. Initially army recruits were *Pathans*, *Rohillas*, *Rajputs*, Arabs and Abyssinians, and later *Brahmins* were added.[54] Friendship was established with Ranjit Singh, the fiery *Sikh Maharajah* of the Punjab, and the *Maratha Peshwa*, and also Sindhia, Holkar, Bhonsla and Gaekwar. The warring *Maratha* Chieftains were finally defeated in the 3rd *Maratha* War (1817-1819), which included the Battle of Kirkee (Khadki) in 1817. [15,71]

This last battle against the *Peshwa* Baji Rao, although not large compared with some, was important in presaging the end of the power of the *Marathas* against the British control of India. The British Resident in Poona, Mountstuart Elphinstone, suspecting the duplicity of the *Peshwa*, withdrew from his Residency. An overwhelming force of *Marathas* charged from Ganeshkind towards a small but prepared British Army of only 2800 men, assembled near the village of Kirkee, in the area now occupied by the Kirkee cantonment. Colonel Burr advanced towards them with the 2/1st and 2/6th Bombay Infantry (later 112th and 113th Infantry), 1/7th Bombay Infantry, two companies of Bengal Native Infantry and the old Bombay *European* Regiment. Captain Forde and the Daupuri Brigade, a force of the *Peshwa* that had turned coat, was on the right flank. The British force only had 10 light guns. However the disciplined British troops routed the *Maratha* force, who fled the field of battle.[71] To this day a road in Kirkee is still called Burr Road after Colonel Burr, despite the name change by the independent Indian government. My home was in Kirkee from 1930 to until Indian Independence 1947, and as a child I used to explore this battlefield. A possible ancestor of mine, a Private in the Bombay *European* Regiment, survived the battle of Kirkee in 1817.

Pillage, rape, slaughter and indiscriminate destruction by the *badmash Pindari*, evil plunderers and bandits in central and northern India, followed with the ensuing anarchy and chaos in 1818. Thousands of villages were ruined and many square miles of agricultural land laid waste. This the British terminated. All the *Maratha* lands in the Deccan and elsewhere were annexed and the British became the paramount power in India, more by circumstance than design, considering themselves to be the rightful heirs of the dying *Moghul* Empire of India. It was the real beginning of acceptance of Rudyard Kipling's *'white man's burden'* in India, to keep the peace, and care for both Indians and *Europeans* in this diverse and remarkable country. On the civil side action was taken to improve the non-existent sanitation of Calcutta. Surveys were carried out of the condition of the old *Moghul* canal system of irrigation and projects mounted to renovate, remodel and improve these. The Marquess of Hastings was said to be *'the first to admit Eurasians to Government House and to allow them the rank of field officers in the Army'*[57] (see Fig. 3).

Englishman William Pitt, Earl Amherst's Governor Generalship in India (1823 - 1828) is notable for the success of the 1st Burmese War (1824 - 1826) (see Fig. 4). Anglo-Dutchman Lord William Cavendish Bentinck was Governor General of all India (1828 - 1835) during the reigns of King George IV (1820 - 1830) and King William IV (1830 - 1837) of Great Britain and Ireland. He prohibited *suttee*, the burning of widows on their dead husband's funeral pyres, and *thugee*, the practice of ritual murder by strangling of innocent people with a knotted *ruhmal* in the name of the *Hindu* god *Kali*, by robber gangs, with the able assistance of Captain Sir William Sleeman. Bentinck also had English made the language of Government and higher courts in 1835, instead of Persian which was prevalent until then. He had government-aided education put on western lines and in the English language also, with the help of Thomas Babington Macaulay, who was also responsible for the drafting of the *Indian Penal Code* (which did not become law until 1860, under Lord Lawrence). With the India Act of 1833 the E.I.C. were required to *'close their commercial business, and make sale of all their merchandise, Stores, and Effects at Home and Abroad'*. They in effect became the British Government's agent for the administration of India. Indians and natural-born subjects were to be allowed to hold high office.[33] By 1833 Christian missionaries were allowed to enter the country in large numbers without a licence, which caused alarm amongst the Indians who feared a British plot to disestablish their religions and social culture.

There were 14 major languages and some 600 minor languages or dialects in the Indian subcontinent. Not surprisingly a single language *Hindustani* became the *lingua franca,* that is apart from English. It had developed from *Khari Boli* (camp speak), the 'standing' or current language of the *Moghul* armies during their conquest of India in the 13th century and

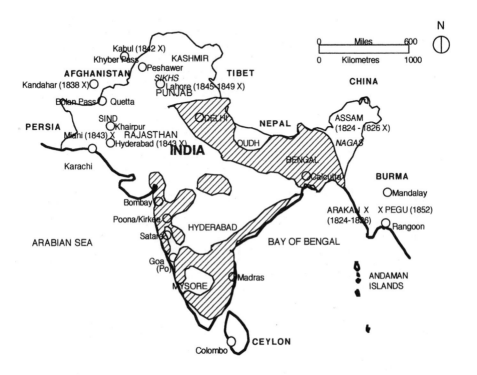

N

| 0 | Miles | 600 |
| 0 | Kilometres | 1000 |

Kabul (1842 X)
Khyber Pass
Peshawer
KASHMIR
TIBET
AFGHANISTAN
SIKHS
Kandahar (1838 X)
Lahore (1845-1849 X)
CHINA
PUNJAB
Bolan Pass Quetta

SIND
DELHI
ASSAM
(1824 - 1826 X)
PERSIA
Khairpur
RAJASTHAN
NEPAL
Miahi (1843) X
Hyderabad (1843 X)
INDIA
OUDH
NAGAS

Karachi
BENGAL

Calcutta
BURMA
Mandalay

Bombay
ARAKAN X   X PEGU (1852)
Poona/Kirkee
HYDERABAD
(1824-1826)
Rangoon
Satara

ARABIAN SEA
BAY OF BENGAL
Goa
(Po)
Madras
ANDAMAN
ISLANDS
MYSORE

CEYLON
Colombo

Figure 4:
BRITISH RAJ   INDIA - 1st BURMA WAR 1824 - 1826
                    - 2nd BURMA WAR 1852
                    - 1st AFGHAN WAR 1838 - 1842
                    - SIND WAR 1843
                         - 1st SIKH WAR 1845 - 1846
                         - 2nd SIKH WAR 1848 - 1849
Note: Po = Portuguese colony
       X = Battle
       = British Territory 1824

after, used to converse with the indigenous people of *Hindustan*, hence *Hindustani*. It was greatly promoted in the late 18th century by Englishman John Borthwick Gilchrist, who wrote *'Dictionary, English and Hindoostanee (1787-90)'* and a *'Grammar of the Hindoostanee Language'* in 1796, as did Rev. Thomas Craven in 1932.[19]

Gilchrist was the first President of Fort William College at Calcutta, which trained British Civil Servants. *Hindi*, which became the main language of *Hindus* and one of the official languages of India after independence in 1947, is alleged to have been derived from *Hindustani*, strongly influenced by the ancient *Sanskrit* language, whose script was adopted. Likewise *Urdu*, the main language of the *Muslims*, and one of the official languages of Pakistan after partition in 1947, is also alleged to have been developed from *Hindustani*, strongly influenced by the Persian language, whose 'Arabic' script was adopted. *Urdu* also remained a main language in independent India.[26] English continued as the second main language of Government, commerce and society, in both independent India and Pakistan after 1947 respectively, and subsequently in Bangladesh (once East Pakistan), where Bengali is also an official language. Modern *Hindustani*, sometimes erroneously called 'kitchen *Urdu*' or 'kitchen *Hindi*', which has a liberal sprinkling of English when spoken, to accommodate modern western intrusion, could and still is generally understood all over the sub-continent. It was compulsory for *Europeans and Anglo-Indians* in the Indian Civil Service and the Indian Army to learn to speak *Hindustani*. It also became essential for business, and for British families to be understood by domestic servants, and in the bazaar. Many *Europeans* and *Anglo-Indians* also spoke a local language, or dialect. *Hindustani* was commonly learned by British children as infants from their *ayah* (nurse-maid), and frequently before they learnt English. It was policy in many *Anglo-Indian* schools to teach *Urdu* or *Hindi* compulsorily.

Bentinck instructed the improvement of hundreds of miles of the old *Moghul* roads by embankment and metalled surfacing, with compacted crushed stone (water-bound macadam), using a system pioneered in Britain by a Scottish Road Engineer John Loudon McAdam in the early 1800s. (His name is better known in the 20th century for tar and bitumen macadam roads). Elsewhere laterite and later burnt brick was used. The vast rivers were first crossed with ferries, and later pontoon bridges, before *pukka*, or permanent bridges were installed. The smaller streams had 'Irish' bridges, or fords. The first Government road was constructed from Bombay to Poona in 1830. This was followed in 1840 by the 1500 mile long famous Grand Trunk Road from Calcutta through Delhi to Peshawer, several hundred miles of which in the Punjab were improved by a brilliant young Irish-Scots Engineering Captain, later to become General Sir Alex Taylor. This played a very big part in transporting the military during the mutiny and helping to subdue the rebellion and reduce its impact on the rest of the country.[21] Other roads followed from Bombay to Agra (900 miles) and Bombay to Madras (800 miles) shortly after.[24] Between 1842 and 1857 the Bombay to Calcutta road, the Great Deccan Road, was built, followed in 1870 by the road from Madras to Calcutta.[65] Bentinck also introduced experiments with tea cultivation and coal and iron production.

During the reign of Queen Victoria of Great Britain and Ireland (1837 - 1901), Englishman George Eden, Earl of Auckland, who was Governor-General (1835 - 1842) and Commander-in-Chief, launched the 1st Afghan War (1838 - 1842), as the British feared the influence of Russia over Persia and Afghanistan. The attack was launched through the Bolan Pass near Quetta, as the Khyber Pass was blockaded by the *Sikhs*. The command was under General Sir John Keane, who entered Kandahar and subsequently captured Kabul. However during a disastrous retreat in 1842 the entire British Army, led by General William Elphinstone, were practically annihilated. The position was reversed the same year when General William Nott and General George Pollock reoccupied Kabul (see Fig. 4). A possible ancestor of mine, a Sergeant Major in the Bombay Engineers, survived the 1st Afghan War.

The colony and protectorate of Aden in southern Arabia became British almost by accident in 1839, at the initiative of Commander Stafford Haines of the E.I.C. Marines.[33] It was acquired as part of a pre-emptive raid on Adeni pirates harassing E.I.C. shipping on passage to India. Aden served both as a naval base and coaling station. In 1858 it was transferred to the Crown as part of British India and formed part of the Bombay Presidency. It became a separate colony in 1936. The Aden Protectorate, the hinterland of Aden, was formed by treaty with the Arab Chiefs in 1873. On 13th November 1967 the Government of Aden and the Protectorate, (then the Federation of South Arabia) was relinquished to one of the freedom movements, the *National Liberation Front* (N.L.F.), and the country became known as the People's Republic of Southern Yemen, and later the People's Democratic Republic of Yemen, with Aden as the capital.[26,78] A possible ancestor of mine, a Corporal in the 1/6th Royal Artillery was in the British Army occupying force in Aden in the 1870's.

At the time the short sea route to India was in use, crossing the Sinai isthmus in Egypt, between the Mediterranean and Red Sea, a route used by the Phoenicians hundreds of years prior.[61] Later in 1838 the route involved trans-shipping at Alexandria and at Port Suez, with first river boat and camel train, and later rail trains in between. These were found to be a better alternative to sailing around the Cape of Good Hope in South Africa. In 1830 British Captain F.R.Chesney (later a General) carried out an engineering survey of the terrain between the Mediterranean and Red Sea, and concluded that the construction and operation of a sea level ship canal between the two was feasible. However no concerted action was taken by the British, even though for a while the great British Engineer Robert Stephenson was involved in 1846, before he was diverted on his appointment as Engineer-in-Chief on the Alexandra to Cairo railway. The French former Diplomat Ferdinand Marie Vicomte de Lesseps formed the Suez Canal Company in 1856. Construction on this enormous 91 mile long canal from Port Said to Port Suez, which was a considerable feat of Civil Engineering, commenced in 1859 under the French Engineer F.A.T. Laroche, and it was opened to international shipping in 1869. The canal which was 500 feet wide, allowed two ocean going ships to pass each other, although one was required to be moored whilst the other passed. Widening of the channel has continued ever since. After an initial period of Direct Works, the construction was put out to contractors, with the Company itself providing scores of huge 10,000 horsepower mechanical dredgers and associated shore muck disposal conveyors. The canal was divided into four sectors, with the British Clydeside Contractor W.Aiton engaged on one, the others being French. About 10,000 Egyptian labourers and 8000 *European* artisans were employed by the Contractors. The British Government at first opposed construction, fearing for their communications with India, and suspicious of French motives and control. However once the canal was opened they conceded defeat, and strengthened their bases and military presence at Malta and Aden to protect the route for British shipping. Ironically once the canal was open the Cairo-Suez railway became unviable and was closed in favour of an alternative routing through Ismailia.[26]

Englishman Edward Law, Earl of Ellenborough, followed as Governor-General (1842 - 1844), when Afghanistan was again evacuated by the British. The Sind, in present day Pakistan, was conquered by the Scottish Commander-in-Chief of the British Army in India, and later Governor of Sind, Sir Charles Napier in 1843. He defeated the Khairpur and Hyderabad *Amirs* at the famous battles of Miani and Hyderabad. The latter was defended against 8000 *Baluchis* by Englishman Sir James Outram, who became known as the '*Bayard of the East*'. The battles involved three Bombay Cavalry and two Bombay Infantry regiments, including the 1st Troop of the Bombay Horse Artillery (later Eagle Troop R.H.A.).[15] The remnants of a store of handmade limestone canon balls, said to have been used by the *Sindhis*, can still be seen in great heaps in Kot Diji fort. The *Mirs* were interned at Saswad, near Poona, in a former country residence of the *Maratha Peshwa*.[71] Napier was also responsible for beginning work on the restoration of the Sind canals and constructing a harbour and town water supply at Karachi (see Fig. 4).

For the first time the important need for railways in India was promoted by Scotsman Rowland MacDonald Stephenson (unrelated to the famous Engineers of that name engaged on this in England at the time), of the *Peninsula and Orient (P.&O.) Steamship Company*, who was known as '*the father of Indian Railways*'. Although supported by Sir Frederick Halliday, acting for the Governor General on his recall, the railways were opposed by the E.I.C., who doubted the skill of Engineers to cross the mighty rivers of India and to overcome the considerable risks from flooding. They also feared that the railways would not be used by the caste-ridden Indians. They were to be proved grossly wrong on both counts in due course, and their false judgment delayed the commencement of the railways for a decade, during which the guaranteed financing of the construction of the railways by contractors using private venture capital was thrashed out (see later & Appendix 3).

Englishman Field Marshal Henry Viscount Hardinge of Lahore, was Governor General (1844 - 1848) when an enormous army of the *Sikh*

Maharaja Ranjit Singh of the Punjab, consisting of 60,000 soldiers and 150 guns, were defeated in what became known as the 1st *Sikh* war, or Sutlej Campaign (1845-46). Hardinge actively participated, aided by the Anglo-Irish General and Commander-in-Chief in India, later to become Field Marshal Viscount Hugh Gough, who had also defeated the *Marathas* in 1843 (see Fig. 4). [6] The first use of *khaki* uniforms, as camouflage against the sharp shooting *Pathans* of the North-West Frontier, has been attributed by some to Harry Lumsden, better known as 'Lumsden *of the Guides*' when in 1847 they first used *mitti* (mud), or *khak* (dust), hence *khaki* (dust coloured in *Urdu*), and later the *mazari* plant to conceal the bright red and white uniforms of the British Army in battle. However *khak* also means waste, including human waste. Indeed I recollect using it as an infant with my *ayah*, when signalling an urgent call of nature! Others ascribed its first adoption of *khaki* to the Green Howards during the 1868 campaign on the frontier. Some say it started with the Boer War in South Africa 1899 - 1900. Contemporary paintings and photographs suggest that perhaps purpose-made *khaki* battle dress was first used by General Roberts and his troops in the 2nd Afghan War 2, 1878-1880.[15,42]

James Andrew Broun-Ramsay, the Scottish Marquess of Dalhousie, Governor General (1848 - 1856), was considered the '*greatest of Indian proconsuls*'. During his time the Punjab was conquered by Lord Gough, with 20,000 men and a hundred guns, in the 2nd *Sikh* war of 1848-49, against a *Sikh* army of 50,000 and 60 guns, and including the now famous but disastrous battle of Chillianwallah, which resulted in heavy losses of British officers and men, including many through what is now called 'friendly fire', but overstated publicly as a victory. He was aided by the energetic General Sir Walter Gilbert, called '*the best rider in India*' with professional advice from Sir John Cheap of the Engineers and Sir Patrick Grant. In consequence the once powerful *Maharaja* Ranjit Singh was deposed and the Punjab was annexed by the British. Annexation of the kingdoms of Nagpur, Satara, Jhansi and Berar followed. The '*doctrine of lapse*' was applied whereby principalities were acquired if an Indian ruler died without an heir of his own blood, to avoid the feuding which arose from contestants. The Kingdom of Oudh was also annexed because its administration was '*fraught with the suffering of millions*'. The 2nd Burmese War was fought successfully in 1852.[6,13,57] (see Fig.4).

Colossal Civil Engineering works commenced in India during this period. Maud Driver in '*The Unsung*' [21] describes the dedication of some Engineers. The Public Works Department (P.W.D.) was started, under Colonel Robert Napier, Government Engineer-in-Chief, later to become Lord Napier of Magdala in 1854. In 1866 it was divided into Military, Civil (including Irrigation) and Railways, and in 1867 into separate P.W.D.s for each Presidency. In 1895 the Military separated from the Civil works. Works included the first Railways in India, a form of public transport developed and first pioneered in 1825 in northern England, by the renowned English Railway Engineer George Stephenson. The introduction of the Railways to India was probably the greatest single contribution to the social and economic development, and establishment of peace in the country.

Lord Dalhousie, who in 1845 engaged the competent and enthusiastic English Railway Engineer F. W. Simms as his Consulting Engineer, entrusted railway construction in India at first to private companies. Railways were constructed to a very high standard, but without extravagance, as quality was being monitored by the government, whilst Contractors were concerned to limit expenditure to ensure profits. Simms was succeeded as Consulting Engineer to the Government of India in 1850 by the brilliant, though controversial, Irish Colonel J. Pitt Kennedy, formerly of the Royal Engineers (R.E.) for a year, before he left and later became Consulting Engineer to the *Bombay, Baroda and Central Indian Railway* (B.B.&C.I.R.). The Consulting Engineers to the Governments of Bombay *(Mumbai)*, Madras and Bengal at the time were Captain Crawford, of the Bombay Engineers, Major Pears, of the Madras Engineers and Major W. Erskine Baker of the Bengal Engineers respectively, the latter, later to become Major-General Erskine Baker and subsequently succeeding Colonel Kennedy in 1851 as Consulting Engineer to the Indian central Government, (see Appendix 3).

The Railways started with the opening of the first line from Bombay *(Mumbai)* to Thana in 1853, part of the *Great Indian Peninsula Railway* (G.I.P.R.). One branch led   to Poona *(Pune)* and onwards to Madras; another to Calcutta and Delhi by about 1871. Many other railway companies were formed, such as the *East Indian Railway* (E.I.R.) and *Madras & Southern Maratha Railway* (M.S.M.), and the *Bombay, Baroda & Central Indian Railway* (B.B.&C.I.). Expansion was rapid, overcoming almost insuperable Engineering problems, bridging wide, soft and deep alluvial bedded rivers, major flood obstacles, and climbing steep, high rocky mountains. With a 41,000 route mile system by 1947, it became the largest and most technically sophisticated railway system in the world. The route mileage amounts to about ten times that of the United Kingdom.

The first railway construction was supervised by the English Chief Engineer James J. Berkley, with English Consulting Engineer Robert Stephenson, son of the pioneer George Stephenson. The English Contractors were Henry Fowler and William Frederick Flaviell, followed by the first female Railway Contractor, the formidable Alice Tredwell, from England, after her husband died soon after arrival. Many other famous British Engineers and Contractors, like Isambard Kingdom Brunel and Thomas Brassey built the remainder of the huge network, during the subsequent 30 years (see Appendix 3 & Fig 12). During the Indian Mutiny in 1857 a total of only about 200 miles of railway was operationally available in the whole country to assist in transporting troops and artillery to put down the rebellion, in unconnected lengths. Reliance had still to be on horseback, and mule and bullock drawn vehicles and forced marches of the infantry. However much better use was made of the railways during the Afghan Wars in the late 1870s and 1880s and latter skirmishes with the ferocious tribesmen on the North West Frontier. One of my grandfathers and his father, both Englishmen, were a Foreman Engineering Fitter and Foreman Boilersmith respectively on the *Great Indian Peninsula Railway* at the turn of the century.

A cheap Post System and national Telegraph Network was also started, with the latter using the electromagnetic Morse Key System developed by an American artist named Samuel F. B. Morse in 1844. It gave crucial warning later of the outbreak of the mutiny of 1857. It helped to save its spread, by preventing the native soldiers of the huge concentration of British Indian Army, maintained for frontier protection in the Punjab, from joining the mutineers. It also led to their timely disarming in the Punjab capital Lahore and precautions elsewhere.[6] It was also to prove critical later in the 2nd Afghan War 1878-1880.[66] In 1865 the telegraph was first connected between England and India, through Persia, Iraq and Turkey, greatly facilitating government.[69]

At the beginning of the 19th century large scale and long term irrigation improvements began. It accelerated after the British Crown took total charge of Government in India in 1858, to improve and assure agricultural output and reduce the risk of famine which was endemic in this populous country. This included the construction of massive irrigation head works, falls and canals. These works were originally renovations of the extensive early *Moghul* canals built between the 14th and 17th centuries, which had been neglected and fallen into disuse as the *Moghul* Empire disintegrated. In north India, the West Jumna Canal, in Punjab province, the 'land of the five rivers,' which was known as the 'bread basket of India', is credited with being the first major irrigation project mounted by the British between 1817 and 1820, with the Eastern Jumna Canal in 1830. Down in the Madras Presidency Sir Arthur Cotton, a renowned irrigation expert, dammed the the River Coleroon near Trichinopoly in 1836 in south India, and many other schemes also. Sir Proby T. Cautley, a great rival of Sir Arthur Cotton, then a Colonel in the Bengal Artillery. was responsible for the 450 mile colossal Ganges Canal, from Hardwar north of Delhi, to Cawnpore (*Kanpur*) completed in 1854, and many other schemes in the Punjab.[69] The extensive irrigation tank systems in the Deccan, which had also fallen into disrepair during the wars and unrest in the 18th and early 19th centuries, were also restored. Even as late as 1940 large areas of Bombay, Central Provinces, Rajputana, Bengal and Bihar recorded famines in the previous forty years, with significant areas registering six or more famines (see Appendix 4 & Figure 13).

In the Sind, in present day Pakistan, archaeological excavations in the 20th century at the ancient ruined city of Mohenjo-Daro showed that irrigation was practised there using the uncontrolled oversupply of the River Indus during summer floods in 2000 B.C. (see Appendix 4). By the mid-nineteenth century onwards excessive shortages of water were experienced in the Sind as a result of the improvement of canals, and the construction of new canal head works and river barrages in the Punjab. The existing Sind inundation canals were consequently also enlarged and extended and head regulators added at the River Indus to improve supplies. Previously erected flood protection riverside bunds were also repaired to better control the devastating floods that swept across the country. Amongst these on the west bank of the river Sir Bartle Frere, the dynamic Governor of Bombay, initiated remodelling works on the Begari Canal completed by 1856. The

Desert Canal improvement in 1900 was   proposed by the charismatic Colonel (later General) John Jacob, of the Sind Horse Cavalry and Sind High Commissioner, to encourage the former Baluchistan tribes to settle down to agriculture. The town of Jacobabad in Sind was named after him, and his name is still revered there as a *fakir* or 'saint'. When I was working in the Sind on irrigation works 1961 -1966, I found his grave was still tended as a shrine, and devotees sought talismans of good health and safety from one who brought peace to their region. An old employer of mine Sir William Halcrow and Partners has provided funds to refurbish the cemetery to preserve his name and that of other British subjects buried there. Many other schemes followed in the Sind (see Appendix 4, Figures 13 &14)

Early canal construction was carried out by the Bengal (later Royal) Engineers, formerly the E.I.C.'s Artillery, who subsequently formed the nucleus of the Public Works Department (P.W.D.) [69] (see Part 1 & Appendix 4). Many were called back to active military duties during construction, such as during the *Sikh* wars and the Indian Mutiny.

Dalhousie also encouraged the expansion of Engineering Colleges, including in 1847 the prestigious   Thomason Engineering College at Roorkee 75 miles north of Delhi started by Sir P.T.Cautley, and also opened the universities of Calcutta, Madras and Bombay. He energetically pursued the eradication of *suttee*, *thugee*, female infanticide, and the slave trade. The Indian Civil Service was opened to all natural-born British Subjects, black or white, and trade, forestry, agriculture, and mining were developed. All this was achieved with the able assistance of Irish-Scotsman Brigadier-General Sir Henry Lawrence,   soldier and administrator, born in Ceylon, renowned for his efforts in settling the Punjab, and subsequently killed in action at the famous Siege of Lucknow, when Chief Commissioner there during the Indian Mutiny of 1857. There was also the outstanding administrator,   his Yorkshire born brother John Lawrence, then Governor of the Punjab, but later to become Viceroy and Governor General of India in 1864 and Baron John Lawrence of the Punjab. He was described as the '*Saviour of British India*', because of his great efforts in managing troop movements during the Indian Mutiny. Another titan was the enterprising General Sir Herbert Edwardes, once Commissioner of Peshawar.[6,57]

4. Third 100 Years - (b) The Indian Mutiny of 1857 to 1900 -

The infamous great Indian Mutiny, or *Sepoy* Rebellion, triggered in the Bengal Army amongst the predominantly *Hindu* troops, and referred to by some, especially Indians, as the 'first Indian War of Independence', broke out in the large military centre of Meerut, 30 miles north of Delhi in 1857. Englishman Charles Earl Canning was Governor-General of India (1856 - 1858), and Sir Henry Somerset was Commander-in-Chief. It lasted into 1859 and resulted in the deliberate slaughter by rebel *Hindu* and *Muslim* soldiers of the Bengal Army of large numbers of both *European* and loyal Indian soldiers, and innocent *European* women and children, of the military and civilian population in Cawnpore (*Kanpur*), Lucknow, Delhi and

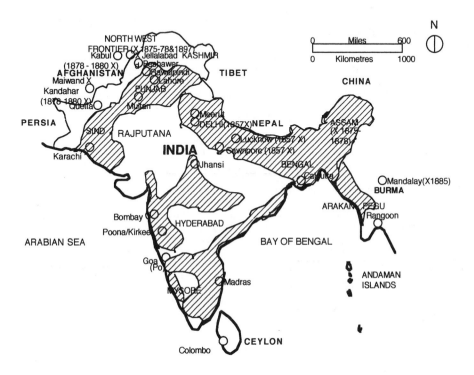

Figure 5 -
BRITISH RAJ INDIA - INDIAN MUTINY 1857/59
- 2nd AFGHAN WAR 1878 - 1880
- N.W. FRONTIER WARS 1875-1878 & 1897
- N.E.FRONTIER WARS 1875 - 1878
- 3rd BURMA WAR 1885-1886

Note:Po = Portuguese colony
X = Battle
= British Territory 1857

elsewhere in the north. It proved a considerable test to the supremacy of the British, to whom it was a great surprise. Most carnage resulted from the mistaken belief of senior administrators and army commanders that the Indian troops were totally trustworthy, and loyal to the British flag, until too late. The cause was not just military, as was popularly supposed, even though it was sparked off by the *sepoys*. It was really a wider reaction of the Indians, supposedly prophesied after 100 years of British domination, to the accelerating development and westernisation of the country, and also the insidious encroachment on Indian social and religious culture by *European* Christians, and concern for the annexation of territory by the British. The Indian *sepoys* earnestly believed that the British intended converting them all to Christianity, by the insidious means of destroying their religious caste by the simple ploy of having them bite their new rifle cartridges, which had been greased with both cow and pig fat, the cow being sacred to *Hindus* and the pig being anathema to the *Muslims*.

The mutiny did not spread to the Bombay and Madras armies and the Punjab remained loyal, but not before the disarming of Indian troops at Lahore, Peshawer, Multan and elsewhere on the advice of the Chief Commissioner of the Punjab John Lawrence. About two thirds of the army remained loyal to the Company. Irish Brigadier General Sir John Nicholson, formerly Deputy Commissioner of Peshawer, who as 'Nicolseyn', is still revered as a saint in India, was mortally wounded at the famous assault of the Kashmir Gate at Delhi. English Brigadier General Neville Chamberlain did more than most to gain victory at Delhi, with the able assistance of the Scots Engineer Colonel Richard Baird-Smith and his brilliant Engineering *aide* Captain Alex Taylor, of Grand Trunk Road fame. The tunnelling below and mining of the walls and gates of the hugely fortified town held by the enemy, which was an important prerequisite to the infantry storming of the breaches, was performed by the Engineers of the Sappers and Miners. This was in concert with the cannon battering by the Bengal Artillery, including 2nd Troop 1st Brigade Bengal Horse Artillery, from multiple gun batteries prepared by the Engineers, who some say were the true victors of the siege of Delhi. The Bengal Engineers were also responsible for 'sapping' their way through the buildings from the Kashmir Gate to the Lahore Gate, so taking the enemy by surprise and greatly reducing casualties from overhead sniping in the narrow alleyways of the town (see Fig. 5) [15,21,66,69].

Englishman General Sir Henry Havelock with a regiment of the Scots Highlanders relieved Cawnpore (*Kanpur*) and Lucknow, only to become besieged in the latter himself. He was subsequently rescued by the popular Scottish General Sir Colin Campbell, later Lord Clyde, the British Commander-in-Chief, who succeeded General Anson who was killed, General Sir Henry Barnard who died of cholera, General Reed and General Arcdale Wilson, with the 93rd Highland Regiment and others. The battle-scarred Residency remains a ruin today, as a memorial to those brave defenders who died there. Lord Clyde was assisted by two brilliant young Anglo-Irish officers, one from the British Army and the other from the E.I.C. Army, both later to become the most eminent of soldiers in the British

Empire. They were respectively Field Marshals Viscount Garnet Wolseley and Earl Roberts of Kandahar. Roberts, the Cawnpore born Deputy Assistant Quartermaster-General of the Bengal Artillery, who won the Victoria Cross during the Mutiny when a 1st Lieutenant. They remained rivals for recognition and success all their lives. Others were Brigadier General Sir Hope Grant and Robert Napier, also to rise to fame as Field Marshal Lord Napier of Magdala, who was the brilliant Ceylon born English Chief Engineer of the Bengal Engineers at the relief of Lucknow.

At Cawnpore (*Kanpur*) General Sir Hugh Wheeler, after bravely resisting the mutineers, had finally surrendered to Nana Sahib, on a promise of safe conduct to Allahabad. Instead, once they reached the River Ganges they were treacherously fired upon by Nana Sahib's sepoys upon boarding the boats collected by him at Sati Chowra *ghat*. His party were massacred, together with over 200 British women and children. Nana Sahib was one of the principle Indian leaders of the rebellion in the north. He was the adopted son of Baji Rao, the *Peshwa* chieftain of the *Marathas*, defeated by the British 40 years previously, who was resentful at not being recognised for a princely pension by the British. Those that survived at Sati Chowra were captured and herded, in very poor shape, back to Cawnpore, and incarcerated in the *bibighar*, or mistress' house of a former British administrator named Sir George Parker. The premises, which were designed to accommodate only one person, were crammed with 180 *European* and *Anglo-Indian* women and children. They had no furniture, and only coarse matting to sleep on, and no bed clothes. Although some of them were injured and sick, and their clothes were in rags, they were not at first allowed any medical attention, or fresh clothing. This was latter rectified. There was inadequate sanitation, and they were plagued by flies during the day and swarms of mosquitoes by night. It was July and mid-Summer, with the temperature over 100 degrees Fahrenheit, with no ventilation, as the doors and windows were barred. Heavy monsoon showers drenched those forced to live in the inner courtyard. The air was fetid and dank. Later they were allowed out at evening. They were fed only a meagre ration of native *dhal* and *chapaties* at first. Meals improved later on, but despite their improved conditions, within 10 days cholera began to take hold, and many died of this.[80]

After two weeks of incarceration, and with the imminent arrival of the Havelock's relieving British force, Nana Sahib and his lieutenant Tatya Tope ordered the execution of the three male adults surviving and all women and children. The three males were first decapitated. Then the women and children who refused to leave the *bibighar*, were fired upon at point blank range, through the doors and windows by the *sepoys*. The result was a blood bath that even revolted the *sepoys* themselves, who refused to finish the job. Instead the *Begum*, the *Muslim* widow serving girl of Nana Sahib's favourite concubine, who was in charge of the women and children, sent for her lover Sarvur Khan. He was allegedly the child of a *Pathan* prostitute who serviced the British Army. Together with two *Muslim* butchers and two *Hindus*, each armed with a *tulwar*, he proceeded to butcher every still living woman and child in cold blood.   The dead and dying were then dumped unceremoniously into a nearby well, to be found by the British Army on their arrival. The flames of the British Army's determination to bring the rebels and mutineers to boot, were fanned exceedingly at the personal witness of their troops on arrival, of the remains of this shameful and brutal massacre.[80]

Colonel William Hodson was another brave Englishman who had fought in the *Sikh* wars, and subsequently greatly aided in the Indian Mutiny, after raising and commanding the famous Hodson's Horse in 1857, a cavalry regiment known as the '*Scarlet Flamingos*'. He was personally responsible for the arrest of the *Moghul* Emperor Bahadur Shah II outside Delhi, but also infamously had the sons of the Emperor murdered. The mutineers had seized the King of Delhi, who was already retired on an E.I.C. pension, and tried to proclaim him once again *Moghul* Emperor. In central India the second greatest amount of carnage and brutality was perpetrated by the *Rani* of Jhansi and Tatya Tope, who witnessed the massacre, by mutineering sepoys, of 66 British soldiers, women and children at Jokan Baghon. Her capital Jhansi was sacked and she was killed fighting, when her forces were defeated by Scots General Sir Hugh Rose, later Commander-in-Chief and eventually Field Marshall Lord Strathnairn. He was sent up from Bombay by the then Governor Lord John Elphinstone, who had successfully prevented a rising in Bombay. General Rose force-marched with the 1st Bombay (*European*) Fusiliers, 3rd Bombay Light Cavalry, 14th Light Dragoons (from Kirkee), one *European* Artillery battery and an Indian battalion, whose numbers grew to 60,000 men, including the 1st Royal Irish Fusiliers. One of my great grandfathers,who was a regimental Apothecary with the Fusiliers, survived this campaign.

Although the British Armies in India numbered 311,538 in 1857, there were only 39,500 *Europeans*, King's and Company's.[52] About 73 E.I.C. regiments of both cavalry and infantry are said to have mutinied.[66] By 1858 up to 1000 British *European* troops a month perished from disease alone, with only a further 100 from wounds.[41]

Terrible retribution was taken by the British on the mutineers, and those captured defying authority. The worst were blasted to smithereens by being strapped to the muzzle of a cannon before firing, to serve as a serious example, whilst others were summarily hanged on the roadside. Others were imprisoned. Those escaping authority were pursued and shot where possible. Villages found guilty of harbouring mutineers were put to the torch. On suppression of the mutiny the Indian Emperor Bahadur Shah, the last *Moghul* Emperor was tried and condemned to exile in Burma. The British Crown, now in the reign of Queen Victoria, formally took over the Government of British India in 1858 from the East India Company. It followed the *Government of India Act 1858* promulgated by Parliament for '*the better Government of India*'. A royal proclamation was made on 1st November 1858. Queen Victoria became the first British Empress of the Indian Empire, although she was not proclaimed this in India until 1877. Lord Canning, already Governor General, became the first Viceroy of Imperial India (1858 - 1862). His position amounted to becoming the Head of State and representative of the Queen, a joint designation that was to be held by all succeeding Viceroys until the granting of Independence to India in 1947. India thus became at last an official part of the great British Empire, and the most populous nation to become such. British India only included that part of the subcontinent that had been governed totally by the E.I.C. at that time. The remaining area of India, or Princely States, of which there were over 500, varying from the size of France to a few acres, remained independent. The *Nawabs, Maharajahs,* and *Rajahs* who ruled them paid allegiance to the Viceroy and were linked by treaty to the British Crown. The Princes retained control of local affairs, whilst defence and foreign affairs came under the Viceroy. The Princes were advised by the British Political Resident in each of the larger states, and collectively in the smaller ones.

Lord Canning was known as 'Clemency Canning', because many felt he had been too lenient on the bulk of the mutineers. In the military reorganisation which followed, the forces of the E.I.C. were amalgamated with the Royal British Army, which latter had until then been rented from the Crown by the E.I.C., or paid for by them by the Government of India. They joined forces under the nominal control of the Crown, ensuring that the army in India should be an imperial force and not a local militia, and with a greater ratio of *European* to Indian troops. Just before the mutiny the total strength of the E.I.C. armies amounted to 137,500 in the Bengal Army, 49,000 in the Madras Army and 48,000 in the Bombay Army, supplemented by 40,000 Local Forces and 39,000 Police, giving a total India Force of 313,500. The British Army only amounted to 38,000. This was found to be inadequate for the emergency and reinforcements had to be brought in from other commands. The army was divided between the three Presidencies of Bombay, Madras and Bengal, with equal numbers of *European* and Indian units (British officered) in the Bengal Army, where the danger of mutiny was greatest, and one *European* to every two Indian units (British officered), in the Bombay and Madras armies. The *European* troops of the old East India Company army objected to the terms of the Crown service and were discharged and replaced by battalions from British Regiments, resulting in regiments of the traditional all *European* British Army operating side by side with the new *European* officered Indian Army, but with artillery maintained in the hands of the British army units only. The magnificent *European* troops of Horse Artillery with the Bengal, Madras and Bombay Presidencies were absorbed into the Royal Horse Artillery (R.H.A.) in 1861. The old Presidency armies were later unified in 1895. The *Gurkhas* were included in the Indian Army.[15,42,81]

In 1860 - 1862 the British Army of India was sent to China under General Sir Hope Grant to protect trade and in particular to restore the legitimate trading in opium from India, considered by some to be the largest British source of revenue from India, and also the activities of Christian missionaries, all of which had been granted by the Treaty of Tientsin in 1858. The Chinese were defeated in what became known as the Second China War, and the Emperor fled when Peking (Beijing) was captured. The peninsula of Kowloon was ceded to Britain, and added to Hong Kong, which had already been ceded in the first China War of 1842.[42]

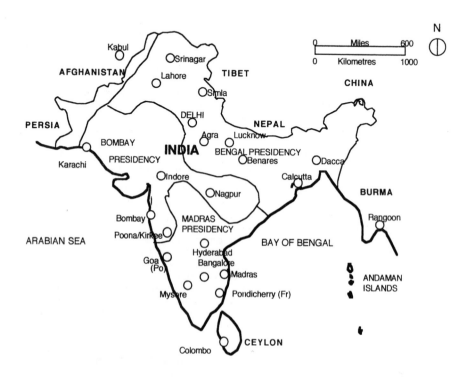

Figure 6 -
BRITISH RAJ INDIA - PRESIDENCIES OF THE EAST INDIA COMPANY
Note: Br = British town
Fr = French town : Po = Portuguese town

The term of Viceroy James Bruce Scottish Earl of Elgin (1862 - 1863) was occupied with consolidating the Crown government. Major land reclamation was undertaken in 1862 which joined together the original five islands of Bombay to form a single land mass. Later, under the dynamic Governor of Bombay Sir Bartle Frere (1862 - 1867), this resulted in a building boom, from which this bustling city, which is currently the second most populous town in India, never looked back. Lord Elgin was followed by the already giant Indian administrator Englishman John Laird Mair Lawrence, later Lord Lawrence of the Punjab, as Viceroy (1863 - 1869). He was the former Chief Commissioner of the Punjab, and the first commoner to accede to this exalted position, a considerable achievement. He spoke fluent *Hindustani* in his official dealings with the rulers of the Princely States. He increased railway and canal construction,[69] pressed for Government construction of the former and public loans for the latter, which were both aimed towards greater agricultural productivity and peasant prosperity. He was greatly concerned about the misery and suffering resulting from the constant droughts and famines in the country, for which he became yet another *European* folk hero, known as '*Jan Larin*', to the Indian populous. He worked hard for public health, prison reforms and primary education also. And to the undying gratitude of the *European* heirachy he arranged the movement of the whole machinery of civil government and administration, and the military command, from the capital at Calcutta in the plains, to the cooler foothills of the Himalayas at Simla (*Shimla*), during the steamy summer *monsoon* season.[6]

In 1867 Lawrence dispatched a British Force from India to Abyssinia (present day Ethiopia) on a 'gunboat diplomacy' expedition which defeated King Theodore II at Magdala. They freed the British subjects being summarily imprisoned there; the reason for the expedition. Some 12,000 troops, together with hundreds of mules, camels, carts and 3000 *coolies* (porters) set sail, mainly from Bombay, in 205 sailing vessels and 75 steamers. They landed at Zula, a Red Sea port 350 hot arduous mountain miles from Magdala. The Expeditionary Force was commanded by Ceylon born British General Sir Robert Napier, of the Royal Engineers, who later as Field Marshall Lord Napier of Magdala was the first *European* Indian Army officer to become Commander-in-Chief in India in 1870, considered a landmark in British military matters.[42] My maternal great grandfather, an Irishman, was a Private in the 3rd Dragoon Guards and later the 18th Hussars with General Napier on this expedition.

Irishman Richard Bourke, Earl of Mayo, Viceroy (1869 - 1872) and Anglo-German Thomas Baring, Earl of Northbrook, Viceroy (1872 - 1876) who followed him, engaged wholly on improving administration. The former was assassinated by a convict during a visit to the Penal Settlement on the Andaman Islands. On 1st January 1877 Queen Victoria was proclaimed Empress of India at a grand *durbar* (court) attended by all the Indian princes at Delhi, thus supplanting the former Moghul Emperors. Welshman Sir Bartle Frere, once Chief Commissioner of Sind and later the distinguished Governor of Bombay Presidency, made overtures to the Amir of Afghanistan during Anglo-Irish Edward Robert Bulwer, Earl of Lytton's term as Viceroy (1876 - 1880), which failed to stop the 2nd Afghan War (1878 - 1880). It had   broken out partly due to British fears of Russia's designs   on Afghanistan and Afghan anger at the British occupation of Quetta in Baluchistan in 1876. The British invaded Afghanistan through the famed Khyber Pass and Kuram valley in the Hindu Kush Mountains, and Bolan Pass by Quetta in Baluchistan. They defeated the Afghans at Jelalabad, Kabul and subsequently Kandahar, but not before a heavily outnumbered contingent under Brigadier-General Burrows, and supported by E Battery B Brigade of Royal Horse Artillery, were routed at Maiwand, near Kandahar. The British Army was under the command of Cawnpore born Anglo-Irish General, later Field Marshal Earl Frederick Roberts of Kandahar V.C., Scottish General, later Field Marshal   Sir Donald Stewart and Indian born British General, later Sir Samuel Browne V.C. (renowned also for being the innovator of the officers' 'Sam Brown' belt). Although the great Indian railway system was of considerable help in the war, the Punjab Northern State Railway, as it was then known from Lahore had only reached Jhelum, the nearest rail head to the Afghan border, which was still some 200 miles or so away near Peshawer, to which the railway was not laid until 1881. It was not opened through to the rest of the country until the mighty River Indus was spectacularly bridged at Attock in 1883,   by a very skilled Irish Civil Engineer in the Public Works Department, later Sir Francis O'Callaghan. Thus provided a continuous rail connection from Calcutta to Peshawer, and a fine road to the border constructed under the supervision of Engineers from the Royal Engineers and Bengal Sappers and Miners [66,69] (see Appendix 3). All travel from the rail head will have been by bullock cart, horse or mule carriage, mule or camel train, horseback or on foot, a slow and laborious mode of transport of the enormous volume of soldiers, army stores, equipment and weaponry required on the campaign (see Fig.5). My maternal great grandfather, who had already seen action in Abyssinia, was later a Gunner with the Royal Horse Artillery in Afghanistan between 1878 and 1880, including being with General Burrows at Maiwand, for which he recieved a campaign medal.

Troops of the Indian Army were also occupied successfully in 1875 - 1878 in several relatively minor Frontier Campaigns quelling the belligerent activities of the *Naga* tribesman in Assam and the *Jowaki Afridis* between Peshawer and Kohat on the North-West Frontier, both in rugged mountainous terrain (see Fig. 5). English Brigadier-General J.L.Nation commanded the former, and English Brigadier C.P.Keyes and Scottish Brigadier-General C.C.G. Ross commanded two Field Forces in the latter. In 1882 - 1885 an Expeditionary Force of the Indian Army were ordered to Egypt, where the *Khedive* had lost control of the Egyptian Army under Arabi Pasha, who had revolted, and there was concern for the *European* inhabitants in Alexandria, and the British owned Suez Canal. Contingents of the British Army from England were also there, as the *Mahdi* was stirring up trouble in the Sudan.The combined force was under the command of the English Lieutenant-General (later Viscount) Sir Garnet Wolseley. The Indian Expeditionary Force was under Scotsman Major-General Sir H.T.Macpherson initially and latterly by English Major-General J. Hudson.[42]

Englishman George Frederick Robinson, Marquess of Ripon was the Viceroy (1880 - 1884) remembered unpopularly for permitting senior Indian judges to try Englishmen in criminal cases, which intensified racial antagonism. He also inaugurated degree classes in the Indian Engineering Colleges, thus permitting the Indians to compete against *Europeans* and *Anglo-Indians* for senior posts in the Railways, Public Works Department and other Government Engineering Services. Irishman Frederick Hamilton-Temple-Blackwood, later Marquess Dufferin, Viceroy (1884-1888) pursued a domestic policy equally friendly to Indians, *Anglo-Indians* and *Europeans*. The *Indian National Congress* was first formed in 1885 in Bombay, after encouragement by the British, spearheaded by Englishman Alan Hume whilst retired from the I.C.S. Burma was annexed in 1886, following the 3rd Burmese War. The British Army, commanded by General Prendagast, and under the new Commander-in-Chief Field Marshal Lord Roberts, defeated Thibaw, *'Lord of the Celestial Elephants'* and King of Burma [42] (see Fig.5).

During the Viceregal term of Irishman Henry Charles Petty-Fitzmaurice, Marquess of Lansdowne (1888 - 1894) the boundary between India and Afghanistan was delimited by the Durand Line, negotiated in 1893 by Sir Henry Durand, Governor of the Punjab. The subsequent revolt of the ferocious *Pathan* tribesmen displeased with this intrusion, resulted in the famous Tirah Expedition, whilst Scotsman Victor Alexander Bruce, Earl of Elgin, was Viceroy (1894 - 1899), like his father in earlier years. The expedition was commanded by Irishman General Sir Bindon Blood, to quell the North West Frontier in 1897, greatly supported by the famous Corps of Guides (founded by General Sir Harry Lumsden) and the Royal Horse Artillery and Bengal Sappers and Miners.[42] The conflict was amply reported by a young English officer in 4th Hussars, who was later to become the illustrious Sir Winston Spencer Churchill, Prime Minister of Great Britain during World War 2 (1939 - 1945).[12] These minor frontier wars and skirmishes, which provided so much active service and excitement for the military, were to continue in some form or another right up to the Second World War (see Fig. 5). Lord Elgin had also to deal with an eruption of bubonic plaque in 1896, followed by the greatest famine ever experienced in India, which affected 70 million people and lasted for several years.[21,57]

In 1899 a movement in China that became known as the Boxer Rebellion, got out of control. The Boxers began persecuting Christian missionaries, converted Chinese Christians and all *Europeans* in general engaged in commerce otherwise, or in running the railways, with a mind to ridding the country of all foreign nationals and influence.The Chinese armed forces were doing little to deter them. An international force of British, American, Austrian, French, German, Italian, Japanese and Russian, and including an Expeditionary Force of the Indian Army, was dispatched to China to protect its citizens and trade. The Indian force was under the command of Lieutenant-General Sir Alfred Gasalee, who later coordinated the attack and successful capture of Peking, following which the Boxer Rebellion was quelled in 1900.[42]

5. Last 50 Years - (a) 1900 to the Great War of 1914 -

The energetic and controversial Englishman George Nathaniel Curzon, Marquess Curzon of Kedleston's Viceroyalty (1899 - 1905) was marked by pomp and circumstance which he enjoyed, including the great *durbar* of 1903 to mark the coronation of King Edward VII. He introduced many social and political reforms, including the prophetic but unpopular partition of Bengal on ethnic lines. Although subsequently reversed, it was almost exactly repeated at the formation of India and Pakistan on granting of Independence to the Indian sub-continent in 1947, with the approval of the *Congress Party* and the *Muslim* League. A quarrel with his Commander-in-Chief Irishman Field Marshall Horatio Herbert Kitchener, later 1st Earl Kitchener of Khartoum, victor of the Sudan, led to his resignation. Lord Kitchener, was the first Commander-in-Chief of all India, after the until then separate Army Commands of Bombay, Bengal and Madras had been abolished in 1895. Scotsman Gilbert John Elliot, Earl of Minto's term of office (1905 - 1910), was renowned for the Morley-Minto reforms of 1909, allowing for better representation of Indian interests in government. He was criticised that his action alienated *Muslims* and *Hindus* and was part of a policy to '*divide and rule*' India which led to Indian partition in 1947. The Viceroy had a narrow assassination escape when two bombs thrown at his open carriage fell short.

Charles Hardinge, Lord Hardinge of Penshurst, grandson of an earlier Governor General Viscount Hardinge of Lahore, followed as Viceroy (1910 - 1916), during the reign of King George V. He transferred the state capital in 1911 from Calcutta to New Delhi. There it's monumental vice-regal palace (Viceroy's House) and Government buildings were designed by English Architects Sir Edwin Lutyens and Sir Herbert Baker, splendid examples of the vast amount of magnificent buildings erected throughout the country during the British *Raj*.[69] George V became the first British sovereign to be crowned Emperor of India, in India, at the Coronation Durbar he attended with Queen Mary in New Delhi in 1911. It was a magnificent affair, attended by most of the 500 or so Indian *Rajahs*, and many foreign potentates, and with all the colourful panoply that only such an occasion can muster. Although Lord Hardinge helped to improve British relations with the Indian Nationalists, he was the target of an assassination attempt in 1912, when a bomb was thrown at him and his wife during a ceremonial procession into Delhi on the back of an elephant. He was injured, but not fatally.

6. Last 50 Years - (b) The Great War 1914 - 1918 -

Lord Harding also advocated that Indian troops should fight, without discrimination, in Europe during World War 1, which broke out between Britain and Germany in 1914, but he was criticised for his arrangements for the abortive Mesopotamia campaign, which was badly managed by English Lieutenant General Sir John Nixon. About 80,000 British and 230,000 Indian volunteer troops were sent to war across the *kala pani*, in the first months of the war, a move which did great credit to many *Hindu* Indians, to whom crossing the sea was supposed to divorce them for life from their caste and families, and also to the numerous *Anglo-Indian* and *Domiciled European* British volunteers. Their numbers rose to a million and a half by 1918. They distinguished themselves with the British Expeditionary Force in France, with the *'Old Contemptibles'*, at Neuve Chapelle and Loos in 1914-15, in an unaccustomed cold winter campaign. They were also at Ypres and Cambrai. Apart from a few sent to East Africa, the bulk of Indian troops were sent to Europe in 1914. In 1915 all but two divisions were moved to the Middle East. They were in action against the German allies of Turkey in Gallipoli, where the Australians and New Zealanders were also involved in what was a terrible disaster. Many soldiers were killed due to bad implementation of a strategic plan devised by Winston Churchill. Anzac Day, April 25th, named after the Australian and New Zealand Army Corps engagement in this battle, is a day of commemoration by both these nations for all past wars. In Mesopotamia in present day Iraq, the Indian Army also played a big part in protecting the sources of much needed oil; first with English Sir John Nixon in the capture of Basra in 1914, and later with English Major General Sir Charles Townshend at Al Amarah and Kut-al-Amarah,   and with the very able Gibralter-born General Sir Stanley Maude, who took over command of the hungry, *'disease-ridden, unhappy, and hitherto neglected army in Mesopotamia'*, who finally captured Bagdad in 1917. Some 10,000 British and Indian soldiers were taken prisoner by the Turks at Townshend's surrender at Kut, and endured over two years terrible privation and cruelty at their hands.[46] My father was a sergeant in the 2nd battalion Dorset Regiment in 1917 with General Maude at the fall of Bagdad. He was invalided back to India in 1918 to Deolali (*Devlali*) near Bombay, where there was an important Military Transit Camp and hospital.

The Indian Lancers also served with the British Yeomanry and Australian Light Horse in Palestine with General Sir Archibald Murray, and later Englishman Major General Sir Edmund Allenby (later Field Marshal Viscount Allenby), who entered Jerusalem in 1917. Great co-operation against the Turks, which led to ultimate victory in Palestine, was given by the brilliantly unconventional and   legendary Anglo-Irishman Thomas Edward Lawrence, known as *'Lawrence of Arabia'*. He was   a British intelligence officer who marshalled the Arabs in their rebellion against Turkish suzerainty. He disrupted the Turkish army by constantly sabotaging the Hejaz Railway from Damascus to Medina, their main line of communication. He then captured Aqaba on the Red Sea, with just a handful of Arab tribesmen, activities for which he apparently never received any official honour. Other theatres of the war the British Indian Army served in were East Africa under General Jan Christian Smuts (later Prime Minister of South Africa), and Salonika, Egypt and Cameroon. They were also engaged in North China and on the North-West and North-East Frontiers of India during this time. India suffered nearly 107,000 casualties during the Great War, including nearly 37,000 deaths from either battle or sickness. Most of the native recruits came from the martial races of India, like *Sikhs*, *Dogras*, *Jats* and *Muslims* of the Punjab and Central Provinces of

India, about half of whom were *Muslims*, and from the *Gurkhas* from Nepal. Densely populated Bengal contributed relatively few.26,77 British Empire Men at Arms during the Great War amounted to 6,704,000 from Britain, 1,440,437 from India, 628,964 from Canada, 412,953 from Australia, 136,070 from South Africa, 128,525 from New Zealand and 59,000 from East and West Africa.46

Englishman Frederick John Thesiger, Viscount Chelmsford, who succeeded as Viceroy (1916 - 1921), introduced more political reforms. They were known as the Montague-Chelmsford Reforms of 1919, with a constitution to benefit the Nationalistic aspirations of the Indians, as a part of British Government policy for *'the gradual development of self-governing institutions with a view to the progressive realisation of responsible government in India as an integral part of the British Empire'*. This was however not without opposition from the emerging *Congress Party Hindu* leader, the English educated lawyer and member of the British Bar turned politician, named Mohandas Karamchand Gandhi, later to be given the title *Mahatma* (Great Soul), by the great Indian poet Rabindranath Tagore. He succeeded Bal Gangadhar Tilak, who had persuaded the *Muslim League* to join *Congress* in 1916. Gandhi had anticipated *Swaraj* (self-rule) for India, following their loyalty and considerable contribution to the war effort in the Great War. It was he who advocated for the Indians a policy of *Satyagraha* (non-violent resistance or non-co-operation) with the British, in protest at India not being granted full self government after the war.32 The *Muslim League* leader Mohammed Ali Jinnah, another English educated lawyer, and member of the British Bar, was also active in protecting the *Muslim* cause. There followed serious political riots and insurrection in the Punjab and Gujerat in April 1919, and following two days of *'violent rioting, arson and the murder of isolated Britons, a vast mob, defying a stern ban, assembled at Jallianwala Bagh, a walled space inside the congested city'* of Amritsar. Anglo-Irishman Brigadier-General Reginald Dyer, the martial law administrator of the Punjab, who was born in Murree in the Punjab, believing he was dealing with *'war against the Crown'*, entered the *bagh*, where a mass meeting was taking place illegally, with ninety Indian and Gurkha soldiers of the Indian Army, armed with rifles and *kukris* (knives) and opened fire. It resulted in the death of 379 and 1200 wounded. Although this firm action resulted in the restoration of peace, it was not appreciated by his political masters, who considered it further alienated opinion in India, and he was removed from his command.8 In 1918 an influenza epidemic caused the death of some 6 million Indians.

Chelmsford was followed as Viceroy by an English Jew Rufus Isaacs, Marquess of Reading (1921 -1926), when the Indian Legislature and Chamber of Princes was inaugurated in 1921, and Burma was made a Governor's province. He was faced with a deterioration of relations between the *Hindus* and *Muslims*, resulting in serious riots.

Lord Reading was followed as Viceroy by Englishman Edward Frederick Lindley Wood, Lord Irwin, the Earl Halifax (1926 - 1931) who had to deal with the continuing activity of the Indian *Congress Party* and their increasing agitation for *Swaraj* (Home Rule) with their campaigns of civil disobedience. Its leading protagonist was still *Mahatma* Gandhi, who captured the imagination of the Indian people by his non-violent opposition to the British *Raj*. He was lovingly known as *Bapu*, father of the nation of India. Apparently World War 1 had encouraged the movement towards independence by illustrating that England was not altogether invincible. His *'Campaign of Civil Disobedience'*, started with his breaching of the Salt Laws. He symbolically walked 241 miles in 24 days to the sea shore at Dandi in his home province of Gujerat, to collect a handful of salt. The direct acquisition of salt was considered illegal, as salt was taxed by the British *Raj*, and was construed as encouragement for others to follow his example. An insurrection resulted and in consequence he and 60,000 activists   were arrested and interned for defying the British Indian Government, and the Press was censored. The call for non-violent protest reached the tribesmen of the North West Frontier, where a group calling themselves the *'Red Shirts'* had formed in 1930 and had to be put down by the British army, assisted by air attacks by the Royal Air Force (R.A.F.), the relatively new arm of the armed services beginning to make a big impact on military operations.[6,57] The R.A.F. continued assisting operations on the frontier right through to the outbreak of World War 2, principally against Mirza Ali Khan, known as the *'Fakir of Ipi.'* [3]

Englishman Freeman Freeman-Thomas, Marquess of Willingdon Viceroy (1931 - 1936), after first   being Governor of both Bombay and Madras, was a brilliant administrator. He was one of few commoners to be awarded a marquesate. He was successful in persuading Gandhi to attend the London Conference on India and helped in the preparation of the important *Government of India Act of 1935*. This included a new constitution, which never came fully into effect as proposed,   in that federation failed to get the support of the princely states. The *Government of Burma Act* was also passed in 1935, which separated Burma from India by 1937. In May 1935 a calamitous earthquake occurred in the city of Quetta in Baluchistan, which destroyed the native city and the *European* Civil Lines, leaving only the Military Cantonment, questionably the largest British conceived garrison town in India, and Military Staff College virtually intact. About 30,000 people were killed in seconds, and as many again later, including many *Europeans* and *Anglo-Indians*. Most deaths occurred in the teaming native quarter of the city. Many thousands more were made homeless, and had to be evacuated until the town was rebuilt. Major-General Henry Karslake, of the British Indian Army, took on the task of rescue and   reconstruction of the town, with the help of Civil Engineer Harry Odin-Taylor.[45] He was one of the Engineers on the construction of the gigantic Lloyd Barrage, across the River Indus at Sukkur, in the Sind, completed in 1932. He was perhaps the first Civil Engineer to design innovative earthquake resistant structures and devise earthquake codes of practice, in the world. My father's younger brother was an Engineer at Quetta Power Station at the time, and received a special commendation for his great efforts after the earthquake in restoring power to the area.

In the 20th century construction of massive irrigation projects continued to improve agriculture in an endeavour to avoid famines which still swept large areas of the land. In the Sind the impressive Lloyd Barrage, better known as the Sukkur Barrage, was designed by Mr. (later Sir) Arnold Musto and built by Mr (later Sir) Charlton Harrison across the River Indus at Sukkur in 1932. It fed a system of 6000 miles of new and incorporated former inundation canals, some of which were as big as the largest English rivers. The area irrigated was the size of Wales. The scheme was considered the largest and most successful irrigation project in the world. Many other major canal works were also completed in the Punjab, United Provinces and Hyderabad at this time. In 1948 the area of land irrigated in India and Pakistan was said to amount to about 60 million acres, which was about a third of the irrigated land world wide (see Appendix 4 & Figures 13 &15).

Scotsman Victor Alexander John Hope, Marquess Linlithgow, Viceroy of India (1936 - 1943) succeeded in introducing provincial autonomy, effectively Ministerial self government, after overcoming resistance from the *Congress Party*. This was during the reign of King George VI (1937 - 1952), who came to the throne following the abdication of his brother King Edward VIII after a very short reign. Provincial and Central government dealt with all issues except Defence and Foreign Affairs, which remained with the British Government. The eleven provinces of British India were Madras, Bombay, Bengal, United Provinces and Berar, Punjab, Bihar, Assam, North-West Frontier Province, Orissa and Sind. The 500 or so Indian Princely States remaining had in effect protectorate status only. Burma was separated from India in 1937.

7. Last 50 Years - (c) World War 2 1939 - 1945 -

On 1st September 1939 the country of Poland, in the continent of Europe, was invaded by the neo-fascist *Nazi* Germany, without provocation, for territorial gain. The German Chancellor and Dictator Herr Adolf Hitler, had visions of Germany as a *'Master Race'*. Great Britain, who had a treaty of alliance with Poland, had in consequence declared war on Germany, as did France, on 3rd September 1939, when Germany refused to retreat back into her own territory, commencing what became known as World War 2. It became a war which extended far further territorially than any other war here-to-fore (including World War 1) as it ranged over the continents of Europe, Asia and Africa, and eventually involved many millions of people, both military and civilian, in most of the nations of the world. Even supposedly neutral countries like Southern Ireland and Brazil in the generally neutral South American continent, had service volunteers fighting for the Allies. The protagonists consisted of Germany, with Italy joining them in June 1940, on the one side, known as the Axis, latter to be joined by the Japanese. On the other side at first were only the British and French Empires, with Poland, Holland and Belgium, known as the Allies. The Allies had not learnt the lesson from World War 1, respecting the manoeuvrability and power of the battle tank, and were in consequence completely overwhelmed by the superior equipped German panzer divisions in Europe. Winston Churchill's elevation to Prime Minister in Great

Britain in May 1940 came in consequence at a critical time. By June 1940 the French, Dutch and Belgians were defeated, and the British forces retreated across the English Channel to England, from the beaches of Dunkirk, saved from a total disaster, by the sterling and brave response of the Royal Navy, Merchant Navy, and hundreds of small often unseaworthy public and private civilian boats, in what amounted to an evacuation armada. From then onwards the British Commonwealth fought the Axis entirely on their own. During the dark and desperate days of the Battle of Britain, in the second half of 1940, the German tentative invasion of Britain was severely repulsed, principally by the valour of the young flyers of the British Royal Air Force (R.A.F.), aided by Empire air forces, including India, and flyers who escaped from Europe, especially Poland. Their efforts continued to combat the incessant, numbing and demoralising German aerial bombings of major British towns during the first half of 1941. Their effort gave rise to the immortal words of Winston Churchill that *'Never in the field of human conflict was so much owed by so many to so few'*.[63] Winston Churchill's leadership and especially his confident war speeches were a considerable boost to the moral of the British nation during the war. One which was especially memorable was following the successful repulse of the Germans during the London *Blitz* when he said that *'if the British Commonwealth and its Empire lasts for a thousand years, men will still say "This was their Finest Hour."'* [63]

Russia subsequently became an ally of the west, when she was in turn invaded by Germany in June 1941, but not before she had already occupied half of Poland. That unfortunate nation was already imperilled by the *Nazis* in September 1939, as was also part of Finland, and the other friendly Baltic nations of Estonia, Lithuania and Latvia. Russia did not end her neutrality pact with Japan until April 1945, shortly before the defeat of the Japanese by the Allies. Although the United States of America was aiding the British with munitions and military arms, vehicles, ships and other equipment, on payment or credit, with the *Lend Lease Programme*, from the second half of 1940, she did not enter the war and become a fighting ally, until she herself was attacked by the Japanese at Pearl Harbour in Hawaii on 7th December 1941 (see later). The outstanding British war loan from the U.S.A. amounted to $30 billion by the end of the war, most of which was written off postwar, when the U.S.A. additionally gave Britain vital economic aid under the *Marshal Plan*. China also formally declared war on Germany and Italy at about this time. Germany declared war on America on 11th December 1941.[14,26,61]

When hostilities began between Britain and Germany, the Indian Viceroy Lord Linlithgow declared war against Germany on behalf of India, before consulting the Indian political parties. In so doing he offended the *Congress* leaders, who called upon their provincial ministries to resign, and in consequence direct rule was imposed again by the British. Some say the response of the *Congress* was prompted more by the failure of Britain to grant immediate independence to India.[24] Despite the negative acts of the *Congress*, India's contribution as a people to the war effort was magnificent. In 1939 the British Indian Army consisted of only about 180,000 regular soldiers, including 13000 *European* and 500 Indian officers. By 1945 the Government of India had recruited, on a voluntary basis, nearly three million Indians into the military services, the largest voluntary recruitment ever recorded in world history. They also recruited a considerable number of *Anglo-Indians* and *Europeans* domiciled in India (see Part 1). The eventual Army was commanded by some 34,500 *European* and 8,300 Indian officers. There were also some 50,000 other *European troops* drafted into India to keep the peace, and to reinforce the Indian Army, who were ill-equipped for modern warfare, as were also the small Indian Navy and Air force. The Indian and *Anglo-Indian* troops supported the *Europeans* with great distinction in all theatres in Europe, Africa, and the Middle East, culminating in 70 percent of the million troops employed in the ultimate defeat of the Japanese in Burma in 1945, with a casualty rate of 27 percent of dead, wounded, missing, or taken prisoner. The latter was in the early years of the Burma Campaign, sometimes described as *'the forgotten war'*, as it was said to have not been well covered in the British Home media, through lack of interest. Also as it had a lower priority with the Prime Minister Winston Churchill and the British Government in London, whose prime concern was to first finish the war in Europe.

In December 1940 the British Forces, under the English Commander-in-Chief General Sir Archibald Percival Wavell, successfully attacked the enemy in North Africa, with the 4th Indian Division, commanded by Irishman Major-General R.N. O'Connor, in the earliest campaign against the Italians. Later the 7th Armoured Division, 4th Armoured Brigade and the 6th Australian Division succeeded in annihilating the numerically (ten times greater) Italian Army in Cyrenaica, a victory not followed-up unfortunately, because of political directives from London. The tables in consequence were turned when the German crack panzer tank divisions of the Afrika Corps, under German Field Marshal Erwin Rommel (later known as the Desert Fox, because of his crafty manoeuvres) landed in Tripolitania. The British 2nd Armoured Brigade surrendered, and the remainder of the British forces were swept out of Cyrenaica and back into Egypt, apart from the brave defenders of Tobruk, the 9th Australian Division. General Wavell was replaced by English General Sir Claude Auckinleck as Commander-in-Chief. The 4th Indian Division, together with the 5th Indian Division, who had first served in Iraq, were posted to the Sudan, from whence they chased the Italians through Eritrea and out of Ethiopia in May 1941. The same month the pro-Axis Iraq nation was defeated by a British army, including the 10th Indian Division, under the English Major-General William Slim. The pro-Axis French Vichy forces in Syria and Lebanon were also defeated in July 1941, by a combined Allied force of British, Australian, Indian and Free French forces.

In the Far East the Japanese nation, headed by their Emperor Hirohito, and ruled by their Premier and Dictator General Hideki Tojo, had opened hostilities against western powers on 7th December 1941, when they bombed the American fleet at Pearl Harbour in Hawaii. The Japanese also expressed the well worn motive, namely that of freeing the orient of the influence of *Europeans* and *'western imperialism'*, as an excuse for their territorial ambitions. President Franklin Delano Roosevelt of the United States of America (U.S.A.), and Sir Winston Spencer Churchill, Prime Minister of Great Britain, agreed to establish a unified military command against the Japanese in South East Asia, named ABDACOM, a command of American, British, Dutch and Australian forces. It was commanded by General Wavèll, successful commander of Allied Forces in North Africa against the Italians, and later to become Field Marshall Earl Wavell and Viceroy of India 1943 - 1947. After their initial conquest of the Phillipines, in the Pacific, against the U.S. General Douglas MacArthur, the Japanese occupied the British Crown Colony of Hong Kong by 24th December 1941, followed by French Indo-China, Siam and the whole of the British Protectorate of Malaya, except the Crown Colony of Singapore by the end of January 1942. The British garrison at Singapore, under English General A.E.Percival, were surprised by an unexpected attack from the Malayan peninsula, commanded by Japanese General Yamashita Tomayuki. It was expected from the sea, for which they were prepared, with special heavy artillery equipped mainly with armour piercing shells (APC) for combat against ships, rather than with high explosive (HE), more suitable for land attack. So although used against the Japanese, they failed to halt them.[25]

Then followed what some consider the most humiliating moment in British military history, when the numerically superior, though untested, allied force surrendered to the Japanese on 8/9th February 1942. Nearly 90,000 Prisoners of War (P.O.W.s) were taken by the Japanese, including 32,000 Indians, 14,000 Australians, and 16,000 British troops, who spent the following two to three years suffering terrible treatment at the hands of the Japanese, in Changi Prison in Singapore, in the infamous Japanese prisoner of war camps in the Far East and in Japan itself. They were also engaged with Dutch and American P.O.W.'s on the building of the infamous Japanese 'Death Railway' from Siam (*Thailand*) to Burma, through hundreds of miles of dense tropical jungle and swamp. The Japanese invasion of first Sumatra, and then Java followed, and with their overwhelming victory over the Allied fleet and airforce in the Battle of the Java Sea, these countries were rapidly occupied by 9th March 1942, with the final surrender by Dutch General Hein ter Poorten, with some 20,000 Dutch, British, Australian and American troops. Meanwhile the Japanese armies under the overall command of General (later Field Marshal) Hisaichi Terauchi had also pushed into Burma in January 1942, and by April had severed the Burma Road, used by the U.S. to provision the Chinese in their war against the Japanese in China, which had been ongoing since 1937. [2,25]

The Burma-Siam Railway extended 254 miles between the existing railways at Ban Pong, near Bangkok in Siam (now *Thailand*) and Thanbyuzayat, near Moulmein in Burma (now *Myanmar*), to facilitate the Japanese invasion of Burma, and ultimately India. It involved the construction of some 688 bridges, or almost three a mile. Work commenced in October 1942 and the line was completed in December 1943, at a rate of half a mile a day, and became the Japanese chief route of supply to the war zone. The alleged atrocities committed during construction by the Japanese, and later Korean guards, on the Allied P.O.W.s, revealed by the

P.O.W. survivors, are alleged to have been far worse than that popularly portrayed in the well publicised book 'The Bridge on the River Kwai,' by French writer Pierre Boulle. An Academy Award American film of the same name, featuring the English actor Alec Guiness was also made. The book and film were apparently only loosely based on the P.O.Ws at Tamakana Camp, and the courageous senior British officer Colonel Philip John Denoon Toosey, who was required by the Japanese to provide labour for the construction of a 5 span steel Warren truss bridge and a parallel timber bridge across the River Kwai Yai in Siam . Some 13,000 Allied P.O.W.'s and between 80,000 to 100,000 Asian forced labourers. consisting of civilians from Malaya, Dutch East Indies, Siam and Burma, were said to have perished during the construction as a result of both Japanese brutality and disease, including malaria, dysentery and pellagra (a vitamin deficiency disease). They were originally buried at the P.O.W. camps, or along the track where they died. The bodies of the Allied troops (except for the Americans who were repatriated) have since been exhumed and reinterred at three special war cemeteries cared for by the Commonwealth War Graves Commission. These are the Chungkai War Cemetery (over 1,700 burials) and the Kachanaburi War Cemetery (nearly 7,000 burials) in Siam (Thailand), at villages of those names near the site of a bridge across the River Kwai Yai. About 6,000 at the latter are said to have been British. There were also about 3,800 burials at the Thanbyuzayat War Cemetery in Burma (Myanmar) (Commonwealth War Graves Commission 1997). Kachanaburi and its cemetery especially has since become a place of pilgrimage.

   The Commonwealth War Graves Commission, with its headquarters at 2 Marlow Road, Maidenhead, Berkshire, U.K., SL6 7DX, cares for individual graves and 2,500 War Cemeteries in 145 countries all over the world, including 35 burial grounds in the Indian subcontinent. These are at major cities, military stations or hospital towns, and include Delhi, Calcutta, Bombay, Madras, Kirkee, Barrackpore, Darjeeling, Digboi, Gauhati, Imphal, Kohima, Ranchi, in India; Karachi and Rawalpindi in Pakistan; Chittagong and Maynamati (near Comilla) in Bangladesh; Rangoon (Yangon) and Thanbyuzayat in Burma (Myanmar); Colombo, Kandy, Trincomalee and Nuwara Eliya in Ceylon (Shri Lanka), and Katmandu in Nepal. The cost of work is funded by Commonwealth member countries, with Britain funding nearly 78 percent, Canada nearly 10, Australia nearly 6, India, New Zealand and South Africa each over 2 percent. Other Commonwealth countries bear the cost of maintenance in their own lands. The War Cemeteries are very attractively designed and landscaped, and are beautifully maintained, even in the newly developing countries of Asia and Africa. They of course only include the graves of those who died in battle, or as prisoners of war in World War 1 (1914 - 1918) and World War 2 (1939 - 1945). They also keep registers of these and also of World War 2 Civilian War Dead (Commonwealth War Graves Commission 1997). Regrettably the graves of the remainder of the armed services, who were fortunate to survive the wars, are left generally unattended, in often overgrown cemeteries, and often in a poor state of repair, as are the graves of British civilians in former British Empire countries in Africa and Asia, as I found in India in 1995 (see photos). The charity British Association for Cemeteries in South Asia

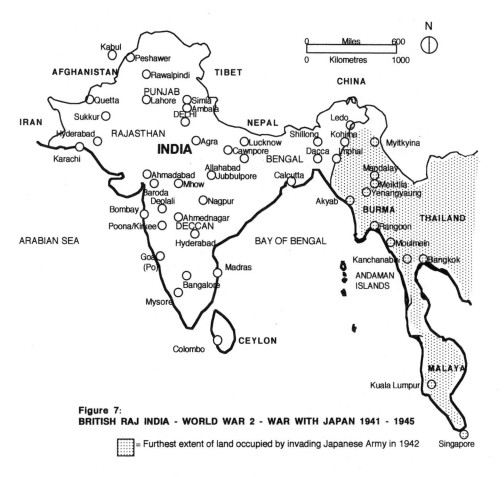

N

| Miles | 600 |
| Kilometres | 1000 |

Kabul
○
Peshawer
○
AFGHANISTAN
○Rawalpindi   TIBET
PUNJAB
○Quetta   ○Lahore   ○Simla
                ○Ambala
Sukkur○   DELHI
IRAN
Hyderabad   RAJASTHAN
○   ○Agra   ○Lucknow
Karachi   INDIA   ○Cawnpore
                Allahabad   ○Jubbulpore
                ○Ahmadabad
                ○Mhow
            Baroda
            Deolali
Bombay   ○Nagpur
            ○Ahmednagar
Poona/Kirkee○   DECCAN
ARABIAN SEA   Hyderabad
            Goa
            (Po)
                ○   Madras
            Bangalore
        Mysore

CHINA

NEPAL
Shillong   Kohima   Ledo
Dacca   Imphal   ○Myitkyina
BENGAL
Calcutta   Mandalay
            Meiktila
            Yenangyaung
    Akyab   BURMA   THAILAND
            Rangoon
BAY OF BENGAL   Moulmein
        Kanchanaburi   Bangkok
ANDAMAN   ○
ISLANDS

CEYLON
Colombo

MALAYA
Kuala Lumpur

Figure 7:
BRITISH RAJ INDIA - WORLD WAR 2 - WAR WITH JAPAN 1941 - 1945

= Furthest extent of land occupied by invading Japanese Army in 1942   Singapore

© Alfred D.F.(George) Gabb 2000

Kirkee (*Khadki*) War Cemetery 1939 - 1945, in 1995

Old St Sepulchre's Cemetery, Hadapsa, near Poona (*Pune*), in 1995

(B.A.C.S.A.), referred to in Part 1, is attempting to remedy this in Asia.

Anglo-Irish Lieut.-General Sir Harold Rupert Leofric George Alexander (later Field Marshal Earl Alexander of Tunis), fresh from his successful command in North Africa, took command of the British Burma Army in March 1942. The allied forces in the north were under U.S. General Joseph W. Stilwell (known fondly as Vinegar Joe), Chief of Staff to Supreme Allied Commander of China theatre of war, Generalissimo Chiang Kai-Shek. The British and Indian troops, known as BURCORPS, including the Indian 5th and 7th Divisions, in central Burma, were first commanded by English Major-General R. A. Hutton, and later by the charismatic English Lieut.-General William Slim (later to become Supreme Allied Commander in South East Asia, Chief of the Imperial General Staff (C.I.G.S.), in England, the highest British military position, and the first for an officer from the Indian Army, and subsequently Field Marshal Viscount Slim of Yarralumla, and Governor General of Australia). They were outnumbered and outgunned by the Japanese, and retreated to Imphal, just inside the Indian border, painfully but in good order. The precaution had been taken by the Civil Engineer W. L. Forester, to deny the Japanese army fuel for their vehicles, by blowing-up the Burmah Shell oil wells and installations at Rangoon and Yenangyaung. By May 1942 all of Burma was in Japanese hands, and India was exposed to the danger of invasion by the Japanese, 'the yellow peril' (see Fig. 7). Louis Allen in his excellent and well researched book 'Burma: The Longest War 1941 - 1945'2 gives a detailed and balanced account of the war in Burma, from both the Allied and Japanese perspectives, listing the regiments and commanders of both armies throughout.

In 1942, with the Cripps Mission, India was offered the long-promised Dominion status, but this was rejected by both the Hindus and the Muslims. In August 1942, despite the Japanese menace, the Congress Party, spearheaded by Gandhi and the Muslim League by Jinnah, tried to blackmail the government by threatening a mass disobedience programme, if independence was not granted immediately, which announced the commencement of the 'Quit India' programme of widespread disorder. Railways were dislocated, railway stations burned and looted, and European passengers were allegedly dragged from trains to be brutalised in Bengal. This behaviour was however not general throughout India, as elsewhere attacks on British service personnel and civilians were rare. Most ordinary Indians were against the British leaving India. Up to 27 army battalions were occupied in counter-insurgency measures over six weeks, an action which played into the hands of the Japanese already hammering on the gates of India. The irresponsible leaders, including Gandhi, were interned at the Aga Khan's Palace in Poona, and consequential outbreaks of violence suppressed. However, undeterred by the divisiveness of the Indian politicians, the British otherwise were determined, following the retreat from Burma, to build up a fresh army to begin a counter-offensive to reoccupy Burma. The Engineers were heavily engaged in improving rail and road links, and building new airfields on the borders of India, involving a labour force of over a million workers, to improve the communications for successful invasion. In the later half of 1942 and beginning of 1943 about 140 new airfields, together with associated buildings, were constructed. Their considerable efforts and contribution in warfare, was little recognised in the success of war. Planning was also instituted for a total of 34 army divisions and 100 R.A.F. and U.S.A.A.F. squadrons of war planes, for the recapture of Burma, Malaya and the Dutch East Indies.[3,51,72]

In Africa in November 1941 the British 8th Army (who became known as the *Desert Rats*) went on the offensive under English General N. M. Ritchie. Although Field Marshall Rommel and the German Afrika Corps were first driven out of Cyrenaica, by the following June they had captured Tobruk and the British had retreated to Egypt. Commander-in-Chief General Auckinleck who then took over personal direct command, succeeded in holding Rommel at El Alamein. General Sir Harold Alexander now became Allied Commander-in-Chief Middle East, with the mercurial English General Bernard Montgomery (known familiarly as 'Monty' by the troops), in command of the 8th Army. The 8th Army consisted of British and Commonwealth forces, including from the latter Australians, New Zealanders, South Africans and Indian forces, together with the Greeks and Free French. In October 1942 the now very well supplied and equipped British Army, including among others the 4th, 5th and 10th Indian Divisions, commenced the counter offensive.[14] They broke out at El Alamein, for which Monty gave the greatest credit to the intrepid Australian 9th Division.[38] After some of the largest tank battles seen during the war, the Germans were pushed back across north Africa 2,000 miles to Tunisia. There they met the Britis-American 1st Army commanded by American General Dwight Eisenhower, with American Generals Omar Bradley and George Patton. By June 1943 the Germans fled Africa for Italy.[26]

On the Eastern Front in Europe, despite Adolf Hitler's treaty with the Joseph Stalin, the revolutionary Dictator of the Soviet Union, the Germans invaded Russia on 22nd June 1941, having totally underestimated Russian resources, a common fault with western nations, even in present times. Whereas the Germans at first succeeded and made considerable inroads into Russia, they were halted before Moscow and Stalingrad, the extreme winters of the country proving very trying. However desperate battles were fought across Russia in which millions of soldiers and civilians died, both Russian and German. It was not until July 1944 that the Russians under General Georgi Konstantinovich Zhukov, amply assisted with aid from the British and Americans, succeeded in driving the Germans out of the country, in their final offensive of July 1944.

Following an easy occupation of Sicily by the Allies, the Italian Dictator Benito Mussolini and the Italian Army surrendered in July 1943, leaving the still determined German Army in Italy under Field Marshal Kesselring. In September 1943 a joint Allied force of British, American, French, Polish and Commonwealth Canadian, New Zealand and Indian contingents, including the 4th and 8th Indian Divisions, invaded mainland Italy, with Montgomery and the British 8th Army landing at the toe of Italy, a joint British-American 5th Army at Salerno and the British 1st Airborne

Division at the heel of Italy. After rapid initial success, the Germans held the line through Casino, in the waist of Italy, until May 1944. By then General Sir Oliver Leese had assumed command of the 8th Army, and following the French Colonial army victory at Garigliano, Polish Corps capture of Casino and Canadian success at Lini Valley, the Germans were once again on the run, resulting in the capture of Rome by Alexander's combined forces in June 1944. But the Germans continued to provide strong resistance to the years end, before Italy was finally released from their grasp.[14]

Meanwhile on the Western Front, following an earlier brave but disastrous attempt, especially by Canadian forces, to invade German positions in Dieppe in France, the combined Allied forces of the west, consisting of the British and Commonwealth forces and the U.S.A., invaded Europe successfully at Normandy in France. On what was known to the Allies as D-Day, the 6th June 1944, a massive sea and airborne operation called 'Overlord' was launched. About 156,000 troops took part. The Supreme Commander was once again General Dwight Eisenhower, with Field Marshal Sir Bernard Montgomery in charge of ground forces in the initial assault. Support was given by Canadian Lieut. General H.D.G. Cerar of the Canadian 1st Army and English Lieut. General Sir Miles Dempsey of the British 2nd Army and the British 1st and 6th Airborne Divisions. The U.S. 1st Army and the U.S. 82nd and 101st Airborne Divisions were under Lieut. General Omar N. Bradley. The Germans were taken completely by surprise, expecting the invasion to occur at the narrowest point of the English Channel at Calais, 150 miles to the north. Field Marshal Rommel was once again the German Commander under the Commander-in-Chief Field Marshal Karl Rudolf Gerd von Rundstedt. The Allies had the superiority of 20 to 1 in tanks and 25 to 1 in aircraft, so it was only a matter of time before they achieved victory. However the Germans fought on obstinately and at great cost to both sides. The Allies were to lose 750,000 troops overall in liberating western Europe.[26,39]

The success of the invasion of the Normandy beaches was partly attributable to an ingenious concept known as the 'Mulberry Harbour', allegedly the brainchild of the British Prime Minister, Winston Churchill. This consisted of a huge array of precast concrete floating jetties, made and floated across from Britain, which when propped on the sea bed formed pier heads, connected to the shore with floating pontoons, which permitted the off-loading of troops and supplies at all states of tide. A surrounding breakwater was constructed by sinking old merchant and obsolete warships and block ships, some of which were supplied by the Americans. The idea was developed by eminent British Civil Engineer, then Brigadier Bruce White, but later Sir Bruce White, of Sir Bruce White, Wolfe Barry & Partners, Consulting Engineers.[82] He was aided by another equally eminent Civil Engineer William Halcrow, later Sir William of Sir William Halcrow & Partners, Consulting Engineers. (They were my employers in 1951). The construction work was spearheaded by Taylor Woodrow, a foremost British Civil Engineering Contractor. Another major innovation which contributed greatly to success of the invasion was called 'Pluto' (Pipeline under the ocean). It consisted of a submarine pipeline which carried fuel for tanks and other military vehicles, laid under the English Channel from the Isle of Wight to Normandy, and later from Dungeness to Calais.[14]

Following considerable aid from the U.S.A., the combined air forces of America (U.S.A.A.F.) and Britain (R.A.F.) engaged in massive bombing raids, of up to 1,000 bombers each. These were first carried out by R.A.F. Bomber Command, under the direction of Englishman Air Chief Marshal Sir Arthur Travers Harris (Bomber Harris), on German cities, principally aimed at industrial targets, in early 1944 and 1945. Massive destruction resulted, often not always strategic. The complete annihilation of Dresden by bombers of both the R.A.F. and U.S.A.A.F. on 13th February 1945, which was particularly severe of civilian casualties, was allegedly requested by the Russians to disrupt German communications and thence reinforcements heading for the eastern front. Over 3,000 tons of high explosive and incendiary bombs were dropped in which about 60,000 German civilians were said to have perished, in this uncharacteristic raid.[37] It is only in recent years that the gross inaccuracy of war time bombing, which resulted in much unintentional civilian casualties, has come to be public knowledge. Immense damage was done in consequence to the will of the German people. The Germans found themselves hemmed in by the British and American ground forces in the west and south, Russia in the east, and with the relentless bombing from the Allied Air Forces from above. Too much reliance had been placed by the *Nazis* on the ability of their advanced and destructive inter-continental missile V1 *(doodle-bug)* and V2 rockets, thousands of which succeeded in reaching targets in England, to reverse their fortunes in the land war, but without success. By April 1945 they had little stomach for fighting the west, as with the end in sight, they had greater fears of the Russian occupation of much of Germany. By 25th April the Russian armies had encircled the German capital Berlin, and Germany capitulated on 8th May 1945.

Only then did the truth of the horror of the concentration camps of the Nazi regime become known, and the extent of the terrible genocide perpetrated by the *Nazis* at Auchwitz and Triblinka camps, with murder allegedly of some 6 million Jews and half a million gypsies, and their cruel treatment of other *European* nationals and Allied prisoners of war. It is all the more incomprehensible that the Nazi regime survived for as long as it did, in a war which lasted nearly five years, and that there was no successful rebellion from within the German forces or from Germany itself, a supposed civilised nation, and furthermore that Adolf Hitler remained the head of state until the end!

In the Far East little could be done initially against the Japanese by the Allied forces, because of the monsoon season that followed their occupation of Burma in 1942. However the Americans under General Stilwell were determined to maintain their supply route to China, by constructing a new 500 mile road, across virgin jungle and mountainous terrain, from the Assam rail head at Ledo, to connect with the severed end of the Burma road to China, an incredible feat of Civil Engineering. They also improved the railway itself to greatly increase its capacity, after being first forced to fly supplies *'over the hump'*, that is the mountains, into China.[84] It was however an ambition they were not to achieve until January 1945. This success was aided militarily by the incredible efforts of the brilliant English Major-General Orde Wingate, of the Royal Artillery (who was born in Naini Tal, in India) and his *'Chindits'*, a Special Long Range Penetration Force. They consisted originally of a mixed brigade of British, *Gurkha* and Indian airborne jungle fighters, who were supplied by air. He introduced a new unorthodox form of guerrilla warfare, originally spurned by the military traditionalists, which proved highly successful. The *'Chindits'*, or *'Wingate's Raiders'* penetrated deep into enemy territory, and were engaged in harassing the Japanese, and cutting off their lines of communication, destroying many bridges on the railway between Mandalay and Myitkyina, in the First Chindit Expedition. They were repulsed in February 1943, and nearly 800 of Wingate's 3,000 man force failed to get back to India, but he returned again successfully in 1944. A separate attack on Akyab on the Arakan coast of Burma, by English General W.L. Lloyd and the Indian Army, was also repulsed by the Japanese in May 1943.

A new South East Asia Command (S.E.A.C.), was created in May 1943, with a cousin of the King Emperor George VI, the charismatic Anglo-German Admiral Louis Francis Victor Albert Mountbatten (later Earl Mountbatten of Burma and Viceroy of India) as Supreme Allied Commander.[84] He was supported by English Admiral Sir James Somerville, Eastern Fleet, General Sir George Gifford, 11th Army Group, and Air Chief Marshal Sir Richard Peirse, Commander-in Chief Allied Air Forces. They were assisted by a brilliant organiser English Air Vice Marshal A.C.Collier, and Welshman Air Vice Marshal T.M.Williams. Also later were American Airforce Generals George E.Stratemeyer, William D. Old, and H.H. Arnold, and English Air Marshal Sir John Baldwin, together with the renowned U.S. General Douglas MacArthur, Commanding General of U.S. Armed Forces in Far East (later Supreme Commander of Allied Forces in the Far East) and Admiral Chester Nimitz, Commander of the U.S. Pacific Fleet, operating in the Pacific rim. The U.S. Burma contribution was conditional upon them being engaged on maintaining supplies to China. The morale of the Allied troops in the Far East was extremely low when Mountbatten arrived to take control. The Japanese had the upper hand and seemed invincible. Although there were many casualties of the Burma war, Mountbatten found that there were 120 men suffering from tropical diseases in hospital to every one battle casualty. He immediately set to work to reverse this situation and was highly successful.[2,26,60,72]

The Japanese had ultimately besieged Imphal and Kohima in Assam, 50 miles inside Indian territory, where the Allies chose to stand and fight for 80 days. Fierce resistance and bitter fighting on the part of the 150,000 British and Indian defenders in the beautiful Imphal valley repulsed the more superior number of Japanese forces under their fanatical Army Commander Lieut-General Renya Mutaghuci, and prevented the general invasion of India. In Kohima some 400 besieged British and Indian troops, held out against 13,000 Japanese attackers. The R.A.F. under Air

Commodore S.F.Vincent played a significant part from airfields within the
perimeter, and under the very noses of the encircling Japanese. This was
the furthest Japanese ground encroachment into India during the war, even
in this their second attempt in spring 1944, under the Japanese Burma Area
Commander-in-Chief Lieut-General Kawabe Masakazu (see Fig.7).
Incredibly, after tentative aerial forays deeper into India in the early years
of the war, in which they got their noses well bloodied by the R.A.F. and
R.I.A.F., they did not proceed as anticipated with a campaign of strategic
bombing of major industrial cities in India, apart from sporadic bombing of
Calcutta, which would have been within their range, due essentially to the
air superiority of the Allied Air Forces. In fact the only significant incident,
which created some panic in India, was what was mistaken for a Japanese
air raid, when in April 1944 a 7000 ton British ammunition ship, the S.S.
Fort Stikine, blew up accidentally in Bombay harbour. Two huge explosions
devastated the harbour area, which resulted in serious damage to many
ships, and the death and injury of many people.[2,28] I can remember being
driven through the dock area as a 14 year old, and being stunned by the
devastation, and being nauseated by the pervading sickly smell of charred
human flesh a month after the event.

The Allied forces went on the offensive again in Burma in 1944, with
the Americans and Chinese in the north, in the Northern Combat Area
Command, under General Stilwell, and the combined forces of the 14th
Army, known as the 'Forgotten Army', under General Slim, in the centre and
south. Tactics included air supply by the Royal Air Force (R.A.F.), and
United States Army Air Force (U.S.A.A.F.), developed the previous year by
General Wingate and his 'Chindits'. It was also adopted by General Stilwell
in the north, on the advice of Brigadier General S.C. Godfrey, U.S. Air
Engineer, to supply his troops. He had estimated that only 75 Dakotas were
needed to do the work of 1,200 two-and-a-half ton trucks, with a saving on
time, and manpower. Only one fifth of the manpower was required for the
construction of new air-strips, as against that required for the building and
maintenance of the necessary roads.[43] The hardship and considerable
discomfort of the intense and all pervading monsoon rains was ignored for
the first time. The troops under Mountbatten's command were mainly
Indian - British and Gurkhas - but they included Chinese, Americans,
Africans, Australians, Burmese, French and Dutch. The British 14th Army
consisted of an amalgam of Commonwealth troops, made up of the British
Army regiments (English, Scottish, Welsh and Irish), Indian Army regiments
(including the India-*Domiciled Europeans* and *Anglo-Indians, Punjabi, Jat,
Dogra, Rajput, Maratha, Baluch, Gurkha, Sikh*, and troops from Gwalior,
Assam, Bihar); also West African Army regiments (Gold Coast, Nigeria,
Sierra Leone and Gambia), and Burmese Regiments. Slim's Corps
commanders were Englishman Lieut-General Sir Geoffrey Scoones, IV
Corps, Scotsman Lieut-General Sir Philip Christison, XV Corps, and
English Lieut.-General Sir Montague Stopford, XXXIII Corps. Englishman
Major-General Joe Lentaigne of 3/9 *Gurkha* Rifles succeeded General
Wingate in command of the Special Force, the 'Chindits', following the
untimely death of the latter, in the Second Chindit Expedition. *Anglo-Indian*
Lieut-Colonel John Masters (later to become a popular author) was left as

Commanding Officer of his former 111th Indian Infantry Brigade, which
included the 4th and 9th *Gurkha* regiments, the 1st Cameronians and 2nd
Kings Own Royal Regiment. Other Chindit Brigades were the 77th, under
Brigadier Michael Calvert, a British brigade that included the 6th *Gurkhas*,
the British 16th Infantry Brigade, under Brigadier Bernard Fergusson (later
Lord Ballantrae), the British 23rd Infantry Brigade, under Brigadier L.E.C.
M. Perowne, the British 14th Infantry Brigade, under Brigadier Ian Brodie,
and the 3rd West African (Nigerian) Brigade, under Brigadier Gilmore.

The troops were dropped behind enemy lines, this time somewhat
precariously by about 70 American gliders, towed behind Dakotas, in
another brilliant though unorthodox strategy proposal of General Ord
Wingate. They were to harass the Japanese and disrupt communications,
in support of General Stilwell's advance from the north along the newly
constructed link with the Burma road. Most 'Chindits' walked up to1,000
miles across jungle terrain and are said to have blown up the strategic
Mandalay to Myitkyina railway, which was heavily utilised by the Japanese,
in about 70 places. Nearly half of the gliders used by the 'Chindits' never
made it to the makeshift airfields amongst the paddy fields, code-named
'White City', 'Blackpool', and 'Aberdeen' after sporting and seaside venues in
Britain, well known to the British troops, 'Chowringi' after a main
thoroughfare in Calcutta, and 'Broadway' after the theatre thoroughfare in
New York. But those that did, provided U.S. Army Engineers, with
bulldozers and the wherewithal to convert the paddy fields into passable
airfields for the landing of transport planes with reinforcements and
supplies, and ambulance planes to evacuate the wounded. Casualties were
heavy. Of a command of 3,000, only about 2,200 returned. About 50 percent
of missing died in action. The remainder became Japanese prisoners. They
had at their disposal almost a small airforce of their own, including
fighters and small bombers, known as 'Cochrane's Air Commandos', named
after the American air ace Colonel Philip Cochrane who commanded them.
Another distinguished unorthodox force was that under the American
General Frank Merrill, known as 'Merrill's Marauders', who had been trained
by Wingate, and fought in support of General Stilwell's American and
Chinese forces who succeeded in capturing Myitkyina. There was also the
Long Range Penetration 'Galahad Force', the first American ground forces to
see action in Asia. The Japanese Commander General Mutaguchi was
replaced by Lieut.- General Kimura Hyotaro for the final battle for Burma.
Lieut.- General (later Sir) Oliver Leese, took over from General Gifford in
November 1944.2.60

Mandalay further south was eventually captured in March 1945,
following a major assault made across the Irawaddy River by the British
14th Army, using fleets of small assault vessels. These included over a
hundred 12 ton timber boats, constructed on the spot, in a matter of days,
from the jungle trees surrounding the army. This was an incredible feat of
initiative and ingenuity by the Royal Engineers and Sappers and Miners,
under their English Chief Engineer Major-General W.F. (Bill) Hasted. He
had also devised an ingenious, cheap and rapidly constructed form of all-
weather road, to permit progress during the monsoon, using woven hessian

(hemp or jute cloth) , impregnated with bitumen, a development which is still used world-wide for temporary road works. On his subsequent retirement from the British Army in 1951, General Hasted became the first President of Loughborough College of Technology (now Loughborough University), the most prestigious Engineering institution in England, which I attended to become a Civil Engineer in 1947.   Earlier the 14th Army had recrossed the ill-famed Chindwin river at Kalewa, across the largest and longest temporary 'Bailey Bridge' ever built. These ingenious bridges were designed by British Engineers, fabricated in the U.S.A. and India, and installed by the Bengal Sappers and Miners and Royal Engineers.

Once the Burma road was reached in January 1945,   convoys once again flowed to and from China, and after contributing to the defeat of the Japanese in the north, the Chinese were able to return to China, where they were still being very heavily engaged by the Japanese.   A Third Chindit Expedition was launched in March 1945,   commanded by Welsh Major General T.W. Rees, with Lieut.-Colonel John Masters as second in Command, to aid General Slim's 14th Army as they advanced south from Mandalay. Rangoon fell without opposition in May 1945, in a combined air and sea operation, with a *Gurkha* parachute battalion,   and the 26th Indian Division from the sea, marking the recapture of Burma from the Japanese. However the mopping up operations in eastern Burma, Siam and Malaya involved further bitter fighting which went on for quite some time.

Of the 29 Victoria Crosses (V.C.s) won in the Burma Campaign, 20 were awarded to soldiers of the Indian Army. The first Distinguished Flying Cross (D.F.C.) in the Indian Airforce (R.I.A.F.) was won there also. After the war a monument was erected above Kohima, which still stands at the Indian border town besieged by the Japanese, at the limit of their invasion of India, with an inscription (based on one in *'Inscriptions Suggested for War Memorials'* (1919) (by John Maxwell Edmonds) to the memory of the Allied troops that perished, which reads;-

> ' *When you go home,*
> *Tell them of us and say:*
> *For your tomorrow*
> *We gave our today.* '2,3,47,51,56,63,64,67,72

The words are repeated annually on *Armistice Day*, 11th November at the Royal British Legion's *Festival of Remembrance* service at the *Albert Hall* in London, to honour all war dead, when the other moving words from the Great War poem *'For the Fallen'*, by Laurence Binyan, are also spoken:

> *'They shall not grow old, as we that are left grow old*
> *Age shall not weary them, nor the years condemn,*
> *At the going down of the sun and in the morning*
> *We will remember them.'*

An *Armistice Day* Parade of the armed forces and veterans is held annually on Remembrance Sunday, at the Cenotaph in Whitehall, London.

As so well described in 'Wings of the Phoenix',[43] written by the British Air Ministry, what was very certain was that without the considerable aid of the combined air forces of the U.S.A.A.F., the R.A.F., including the other Empire Air Forces such as the Royal Australian Air Force (R.A.A.F.), Royal New Zealand Air Force (R.N.Z.A.F.) and Royal Indian Air Force (R.I.A.F.), the defeat of the Japanese in Burma would not have been feasible. Their considerable support in bombing the Japanese positions, and flying in ammunition and supplies into often very mountainous territory, covered by impenetrable jungle, to troops often behind enemy lines, or otherwise besieged   by the Japanese, was a considerable feat of daring and airmanship. They were able to maintain air supremacy, greatly helping the morale of the troops on the ground who relied on them, and made victory possible. In 1941 there were only 25,000 troops, 16 R.A.F. Buffalo fighters, and 1 American Volunteer Force of Kittihawks (P.40) in Burma, to do battle against the Japanese. The odds for the R.A.F. were worse than at the 'Battle of Britain'. In early 1942 there were only four airfields with modern all weather runways which were serviceable in the Command. After considerable effort in terrible conditions, and with the aid of massive assistance from the American Engineers and their heavy engineering equipment, by the end of the monsoon of 1943 some 285 airfields had been constructed, and more planned. Of these 45 were handed to the U.S.A.A.F., with the remainder coming under the R.A.F.. The number of planes also increased as airfields became available, although the war in Europe took first priority. The number of R.A.F. planes rose to 3,699 of all kinds by the end of 1943, 'crystallising to 519 front line aircraft'. The U.S.A.A.F. striking power was raised to 265 aircraft. The R.A.F. was operating 48 squadrons and the U.S.A.A.F. 17 squadrons. In general amongst the planes used by the R.A.F. were the Lockheed Hudson, Bristol Blenheim, and Vickers Wellington bombers, the Republic Thunderbolt (P47), Bristol Beaufighter, ~~English Electric~~ Lightning (P38) and the remarkable all-wood De Havilland Mosquito fighter bombers, and the Vultee Vengeance dive bombers. Supreme amongst the planes were the Hawker Hurricane fighters,   and the   magnificent Supermarine Spitfire fighters, who were more than a match for the Japanese Zero and Nakajuma fighter planes. Allied with these were the much loved workhorse plane, the Douglas (Dakota) transport planes, the DC2 and DC3, and the strengthened DC3 (C47), many of which survive in service today, used by both air forces. There were even the aged Westland Lysanders, and Short Sunderland Flying boats, De Havilland Tiger Moth biplanes, the old Fox Moths and some Westland helicopters being used as air ambulances, extricating the wounded from perilous jungle strips. The U.S.A.A.F. also had Liberator (P24) and Boeing Flying and Super Fortress (B29) bombers, and North American Mitchell (B25) fighter bombers, North American Mustang (P51), Kittihawk (P40), Mohawk, Brewster Buffalo fighters, and Grumman Sentinel and Sikorsky Hoverfly helicopter ambulance planes.[3,43,64,68]   A brother-in-law of mine was a Flying Officer in the R.A.F piloting Beaufighters and Mosquitoes during the war.

Tribute should also be paid for the success in the Burma war to the Royal Navy, based at Trincomalee in Ceylon, and including the Royal Indian Navy, who Churchill said 'had achieved undisputed command of the sea.'[14]

Also to the Engineers, both British and American who *'wrought many wonders of improvisation and achievement, such as laying nearly 3000 miles of pipeline across river, forest and mountain.'*[14] In honour of the great deeds of all the services in South East Asia Command, George VI in May 1945 *'commanded that a special decoration, the "Burma Star" should be struck'* for all participating personnel.[14] Annual reunions of the *Burma Star Association* have been held in London ever since.

E.N.S.A. (Entertainments National Service Association) did a splendid job in raising the morale of the troops and spawned many famous performers like Dame Vera Lynn, known as the *'Sweetheart of the Forces'* and George Formby (after whom I received my nickname, as I played the ukelele in school), the cheeky Lancastrian troubadour, whose swinging banjolele and saucy songs were a joy to so many.

In 1941 an Indian *Hindu* nationalist, by the name of Subhas Chandra Bose, sometime President of the Indian Congress Party, fled to Berlin, where he endeavoured to gain Hitler's support for the ousting of the British from India. Hitler was not too sympathetic, but humoured him by allowing him to form an Indian regiment, after a delay of eighteen months, from amongst consenting Indian prisoners of war in Germany. But they never went to battle, primarily because by then Japan was at war with the British and the Allies. Bose then offered to support the Japanese in Burma, in 1943, where he supposedly set up a provisional government of Free India, and formed the Indian National Army (I.N.A.), composed of 40,000 Indian prisoners of war taken by the Japanese, army deserters, and overrun Indian residents. Up to 16,000 Indian P.O.W.s apparently consented to join this army, but not before they were threatened by the Japanese about a far worse fate in labour camps, if they did not. They are alleged to have advanced 150 miles into Indian territory in 1944 with the Japanese.[46] Bose had been gambling on a groundswell rising of Indians in India, against the so-called British yoke, once the knowledge of the formation of the I.N.A., and its alliance with the Japanese became known. In the event all news of Bose and the I.N.A. activities was heavily censored in all British media, preventing any such risk from materialising. Bose died in an accidental plane crash in 1945, after the Japanese surrendered, which some allege was contrived. The 20,000 or so captured traitorous Indian troops of the Indian National Army were after a summary enquiry, set free and, where applicable, dishonourably discharged from the Indian Army, a far worse and shameful fate than any military punishment, as employment in the British Indian Army was lucrative, greatly sought after, and highly respected by fellow Indians, in all levels of society. Only three officers, one *Hindu*, one *Sikh* and one *Muslim* were tried for treason against the King Emperor and murder of fellow prisoners. All were found guilty but ultimately set free.[46,61]

What is not widely publicised is the enormous economic contribution also made by India to the World War 2 Allied war effort. The development of their industries and opening up of their natural resources by the British, enabled the production of military supplies and ordnance necessary, not only for the defence of India, but also for the Allied armies in North Africa and the Middle-East, transforming by ten-fold the industrial base of the country. New resources were exploited and the old Indian industry of shipbuilding was also revived successfully.26 My father and two uncles were in a reserved occupation in the Royal Ordnance (Small Arms) Factory in Kirkee, near Poona during the war.

On 8th May 1945, now known as *V.E. Day* (Victory in Europe) by the Allies in celebration, the war in Europe officially ended with the defeat of the armed forces of the Axis Third Reich of Nazi Germany and Fascist Italy, by the Allied forces, comprising the armies of the British Empire and Commonwealth, United States of America, Russia, France, Holland and Belgium. It culminated in the Nazi unconditional surrender, but not before the Allies had invaded, occupied and carried out terrible destruction of their homelands, and overseas colonies in the process, especially their industrial towns. The Italian Fascist Dictator Benito Mussolini had already resigned in 1943. He was publicly executed in 1945, by Italian partisans, just two days before the German *Nazi Führer* (leader) Adolf Hitler, is alleged to have committed suicide in his command bunker in Berlin, moments before the final victory of the Allies over the Axis forces. Field Marshal Bernard Montgomery (later to become 1st Viscount Montgomery of Alamain), Commander of Allied Ground Forces, accepted the capitulation of all German forces in North-West Germany from Admiral Friedeburg, emissary of Grand Admiral Doenitz, the nominated successor as leader of Germany, at Luneburg Heath, on 4th May 1945. The Germans in the Italian campaign had already surrendered the day before to the Field-Marshal Sir Harold Alexander. General capitulation came with the signing of the document of unconditional surrender on 7th May 1945 in Rheims, in France, at the headquarters of American General Dwight Eisenhower, Supreme Allied Commander (who ironically was of immigrant stock originating from the Rhineland), later to become President of the U.S.A.. Signing of the instrument was by the senior Nazi General Alfred Jodl and American Lieut.-General Bedell Smith, with Russian and French witnesses. Formal ratification by the German High Command took place in Berlin, on 9th May 1945, with signing being carried out by the Scottish Air Chief Marshal Arthur Tedder (later 1st Baron Tedder of Glenguin), on behalf of Eisenhower, General Georgi Zhukov (the conqueror of Berlin) for Russia, and Nazi Field-Marshal Wilhelm Keitel (signatory to the French armistice of 1940) for Germany. A proper peace treaty was never signed, as was the case with Japan.

The Nuremberg War Crimes Trial, which followed in 1946, dealt with the punishment for war crimes, and crimes against humanity, of the 21 surviving Nazi leaders. These included deputy leader Reich-Marshal Herman Goering of the German Airforce the Luftwaffe, Rudolf Hess, deputy leader after Goering (who tried to broker an Anglo-German peace in 1941, with a daring flight to Scotland), Albert Speer, Minister of Armaments, Joachim von Ribbentrop, Foreign Minister, Martin Bormann, Party Chancellor, Field-Marshal Keitel, General Jodl, and other offenders, for the widespread destruction and atrocities committed by the *Nazis*. This included the terrible suffering and murder of millions of Jews and Christians alike, both

German and foreign, civil and military, inside and outside Germany, not to mention the maltreatment of hundreds of Allied prisoners of war, in the infamous *Nazi* concentration camps. The main perpetrators of this cruelty, namely Heinrich Himmler, the chief of the dreaded and cruel *Gestapo* secret police and Joseph Goebells, Head of Propaganda, escaped trial by committing suicide, as did Goering after the trial, but before sentence was executed.26,53

During this time the Allies, and in particular the Americans, Australians and New Zealanders, were actively engaged in ejecting the Japanese from the Far East and Pacific islands, starting with the Phillipines, where this time General MacArthur was successful against the Japanese commander General Yamashita Tomoyuki. Nearly every island in the Pacific war zone was hard won, as the religiously fanatical Japanese died for their Emperor, rather than surrender, even resorting to *kamakazi* (suicide) bombing of the U.S. fleet. In this MacArthur was greatly assisted by Admiral Nimitz and the U.S. fleet. Great credit for success in the Pacific should also go to the the U.S.Army Engineers, especially in repairing and constructing new airfields, under very trying circumstances, which ultimately permitted and safeguarded the bombing of Japan itself. Under the leadership of U.S. General Curtiss E. Le May, head of the U.S. Army Air Force, a policy of indiscriminate bombing of Japanese mainland cities was engaged in, in an attempt to hasten the end of the Pacific war. A fire bombing raid using napalm was carried out on Tokyo in March 1945, aimed at both military and civilian targets, which was said to have killed 10,000 people, and left a million homeless. The similar bombing of up to 63 other cities followed in which more casualties were said to have resulted than were suffered by the Japanese forces in the war.

In July 1945, by the *Declaration of Potsdam*, Japan was issued an ultimatum by President Harry Truman of U.S.A., Prime Minister Winston Churchill of Great Britain, and Generalissimo Chiang Kai-Shek, President of China, to surrender unconditionally, or suffer defeat and ruination of their country. Failing the receipt of a satisfactory response from Japan, the first ever non-orthodox, but far more explosive and destructive atomic bomb, was dropped by the American airforce on Hiroshima in Japan on 6th August 1945. There was said to be some 139,000 victims of the raid, of which half were killed outright. It laid waste to an area of over 4 square miles. A second devastating bomb was dropped on Nagasaki three days later, although with relatively less carnage, amounting to some 49,000 victims.38 The U.S.S.R. only declared war on Japan on 8th August 1945. On 15th August 1945, now known as 'V.J. Day' (Victory against Japan), by the Allies in celebration, as a direct consequence of the dropping of the atomic bombs, the Japanese surrendered unconditionally to the Allies.

The United States General Douglas MacArthur, Supreme Commander of Allied Powers in the Pacific, accepted the Japanese surrender from Foreign Minister Shigemitsu Mamoru, on board the U.S. Battleship 'Missouri', in Tokyo bay, on 2nd September 1945. The British Lieut. General (later Sir) Arthur E. Percival (who had earlier surrendered to the

Japanese at the battle of Singapore), and U.S. Lieut. General Jonathan M. Wainwright (who had also earlier surrendered to the Japanese in the battle of the Philippines) attended the ceremony. The Royal Navy was represented by the British battleship H.M.S. *'Duke of York'*, flying the flag of Scottish Admiral Sir Bruce Fraser. The document of surrender of the Japanese was, in addition to the Japanese, signed by representatives of all the Allies participating, namely Great Britain, United States of America, United Soviet Socialist Republics, China, Australia, France, Canada, Netherlands and New Zealand. The Allied forces reoccupied Singapore on 5th September 1945 and on 12th September 1945 Mountbatten accepted the surrender of nearly 680,000 Japanese troops in South East Asia, in the presence of representatives of the United States, India, Australia, China, France and Holland, and triggered the release of the 100,000 or so Allied P.O.W.s in the region. Unlike the situation in Germany and Italy, the Japanese leader Emperor Hirohito survived the war as Emperor, with the agreement of the Allies, and without any apparent punishment for war crimes.[9,26,60] The Japanese Peace Treaty was not finally signed until 1951. In Ben Fenton's *Daily Telegraph* article of 19th August 1995

> *'Of almost 800 Japanese convicted by British war crimes courts, 220 were executed. But documents show that the remainder, including many involved in the torture and murder of prisoners, were released within 11 years. ......clemency was granted by other Allies, led by the Americans, who were particularly concerned to encourage a pro-western attitude among the Japanese leadership. ....none of the major Class A criminals, sentenced by an international tribunal in Tokyo - the Far East equivalent of the Nuremberg trials - served his full time. Seven were executed, including the wartime Prime Minister Hideki Tojo. But of the 16 sentenced to life, all were freed on parole by April 1956. ..... as early as November 1946 Emperor Hirohito was allowed to issue an amnesty to all Japanese soldiers accused of crimes. .....in 1950 General Douglas MacArthur, the Supreme Allied Commander in the Far East, agreed that all war criminals serving less than 10 years should be released the following year. Finally, in 1955, the new Prime Minister, Anthony Eden, and the Foreign Secretary, Harold Macmillan, succumbed to Japanese pressure to free the remaining prisoners.'*
> ("© Telegraph Group Limited, London 1995").

It appears this appalling leniency, on purely political grounds, was never revealed to the Allied and British public in general, and the veterans of the war in particular, and both military and civilian P.O.W.s, at the time, not becoming generally known until the 50th anniversary of the end of the war in 1995. In consequence, even as late as the 50th anniversary of 'V.J. Day', the Japanese people and Government had still not properly apologised to the Allies for their aggressive warfare, nor shown any remorse towards the atrocities and general maltreatment inflicted on the Allied military and civilian P.O.W.s, in complete contravention of the Geneva Convention defining the treatment of prisoners of war and civilians. This attitude of the Japanese people to not face up to their past is further compromised by the words on a sign outside the Yasukuni Shrine in Tokyo, dedicated to all Japanese soldiers who died in wars since 1868, and which is equivalent to the British war memorial in London, the Cenotaph. It says *'It was Europe and America which were the authors of abominable aggression in Asia'*. Ironically the words are allegedly those of Radhabinod Pal, an Indian who was the sole dissenting judge at the Tokyo war crimes tribunal.

Details of the casualties of World War 2 are unreliable, especially respecting the U.S.S.R. and China, where the numbers were the greatest. Estimates of deaths in all theatres of war, both military and civilian, vary between 35 and 60 million people. Of these the loss to Great Britain amounted to about 265,000 military and 93,000 civilians, and to India about 25,000 military, together a sad but mercifully small relative percentage of the losses to the enemy Axis powers and other nations. Together with the remainder of the British Commonwealth the military deaths rise to about 374,000, and civilian 252,000. In Burma, one in four casualties in action were said to have been due to 'friendly fire', that is from accidental fire from one's own side.   U.S.A. lost about 293,000 military, U.S.S.R. 11 million, China 1.3 million, France 214,000 and Netherlands 8,000. Civilian losses were about 6,000, 7 million, unknown, 350,000 and 200,000 respectively. Many more were wounded or taken prisoner. The Axis lost nearly 7 million military dead and 2 million civilians.[26] In Burma alone there were about 74,000 British and Commonwealth casualties during World War 2, either killed, wounded, missing or prisoners-of-war. Of these 14,326 were killed, including 4,037 (28%) British, 6,566 (46%) Indian, 858 (6%) African and 1,636 (11%) unspecified other ranks, and 947 (7%) officers, together with a further 249 (2%) from the Burma Army in the 1st Burma campaign.[2] It was not until 2000 that beautiful wrought iron memorial gates costing £1million were to be erected by the British Government at Hyde Park Corner in London, to commemorate the Indian, African and Caribbean Commonwealth troops who fought and died so courageously worldwide for the British Empire in World War 1, 1914-1918 and World War 2, 1939-1945; the first real monumental recognition of their great contribution to victory and peace in the world.

8. Indian Independence 1947 -

After the war the inspired Prime Minister Winston Spencer Churchill of Great Britain, and his Conservative Party, who had successfully buoyed-up the British nation and Empire throughout the war, and led the British to victory over the *Nazis* and Japanese, were ousted almost thanklessly by the British nation, and replaced in 1945 by the socialist Labour Party of Clement Attlee (subsequently 1st Earl Attlee) the new Prime Minister. His avowed policy was to divest Great Britain of its great Indian Empire, and indeed the remainder of the British Empire also. Winston Churchill, who it was considered never liked nor trusted the Indians, was always against self-government for India.

Much political and sectarian unrest amongst the Indians, and general unrest amongst the British troops occurred at this time, with the end of

Figure 8:
BRITISH RAJ INDIA   BEFORE INDEPENDENCE IN 1947

Legend: ☐ = British India

▨ = Princely States

NWFP = North West Frontier Province

Figure 9:
INDIA AND PAKISTAN AFTER INDEPENDENCE IN 1947

Legend: PEPS = Patiala & East Punjab States
      B   = Bhopal
      VP   = Vindhya Pradesh
      MB = Madhya Bharat
      HP = Himachal Pradesh

the war and the expectation of Indian self rule, which included the prospect of separate nations for the *Hindus* and *Muslims* of India. In British units of the Royal Air Force at Drig Road Airport near Karachi, B.O.R.s, many of whom were only war time conscripts, mutinied in January 1946, but without violence, in protest at the slow pace of repatriation back to England. This was followed by others in India, Ceylon and the Middle East who were since 1944 under the command of Air Chief Marshal Sir Keith Parkes. They felt that having been conscripted for the war against the Germans and Japanese, which was then over, the British Government had no right to use them for what amounted to political policing in India and the Far East. At first the ring leaders were court martialled and imprisoned. Others returned to duties under threat of execution by their commanding officers. In the event public opinion in England came to their aid and demobilisation soon began in 1947. As a youth I travelled back to England in May 1947 aboard the *'Empress of Scotland'* with about 2,000 British troops due for demobilisation. It was one of the last troop ships to leave India.

Encouraged by the action of the R.A.F., the Royal Indian Air Force also became insubordinate, declaring their sympathy with the Indian National Army in their frustration. The ratings of the Royal Indian Navy, whose officers were all *European*, also mutinied in Bombay, Calcutta, Madras and Karachi, impatient at the slow pace towards self government. Bombers of the R.A.F. intimidated the navy, and the military were called out, including the Indian Army, and succeeded in subduing the mutineers, but not before the R.I.N. had trained their guns threateningly on Bombay city, and the mutineers had taken many casualties at Karachi.[23] On 23rd February 1946 the *'Times of India'* newspaper reported over 700 casualties in Bombay riots, including 59 deaths. The British Army opened fire on rioters and looters to restore order. Naval ratings attacked trains and buses, government offices and *Europeans* and persons in western attire. Later followed continuous political disharmony in India, with clashes between *Hindus* and *Muslims* resulting in the murder of many thousands mainly in the teaming cities of Calcutta, Lahore, Amritsar and Bombay. In what was known as *'the great Calcutta killings'* between 5,000 and 6,000 people were killed and 15,000 injured in riots. Gandhi and Pandit Jawaharlal Nehru, another English educated lawyer and member of the British Bar, supposedly representing all Indians and 60,000 of their *Congress Party* supporters were imprisoned by the British Government. Disillusioned *Muslims* transferred their allegiance to the *Muslim League* and Jinnah.[59]

The British Government in London finally announced in February 1947 their intention of transferring power to the Indians by June 1948. Earl Wavell, Viceroy of India since 1943, resigned in protest, as he, as with Winston Churchill, did not agree with this decision. He was succeeded by the last Viceroy of India   Admiral Lord Louis Mountbatten, Earl Mountbatten of Burma, to oversee the rapid transfer of power and with unprecedented plenipotentiary powers to do so, following his successful leadership of the Allied victory over the Japanese in Burma and the Far East in 1945. Lord Mountbatten was ably assisted by Field Marshal Sir

Claude Auckinleck   as Commander-in-Chief in India, and Englishman General Lord Hastings Lionel Ismay, who was born in Naini Tal, as his Chief of Staff. He was also supported by the 11 Governors of the provinces, including Scotsman Sir John Colville (later Lord Clydesmuir) of the Bombay Presidency and Sir Archibald Nye of the Madras Presidency, who were to be invited by the Indians to stay on as Governors after Indian Independence. Unrest in the country continued and the prospects for a united India receded. Soon after Mountbatten's arrival violence erupted in the North West Frontier with a crowd of up to 100,000 *Pathans* allegedly threatening to march on Government House. Mountbatten personally flew to Peshawer and confronted them, won their confidence and persuaded them to disperse peaceably. The state of affairs was inexorably advancing towards civil war between the *Muslims* who desired their own nation, and the remainder of India. Urgent positive action was imperative. After protracted discussions with Gandhi, Nehru and Jinnah, Mountbatten finally announced that the only solution lay in the division of the country into two separtae states, based essentially on religious and ethnic grounds. The *India Independence Act 1947* became law at midnight on 14th August 1947, as *Hindu* astrologers thought that the 15th August 1947, *Independence Day*, was inauspicious.[84]

The two independent Dominion states of Pakistan (land of the pure) with a majority of *Muslims*, and India, with a majority of *Hindus*, came into being, nearly 12 months ahead of the original programme. Cries of '*Jai Hind*' (long live India) or '*Bharat ke jai*' (may India flourish), by the new Indians, and '*Pakistan Zindabad*' (long live Pakistan), by the Pakistanis were shouted abroad. India chose to keep the name of 'India', with its capital at New Delhi, rather than *Hindustan* as it was known by the *Moghuls*, or *Bharat* a popular ancient name for India. The new India leader Pandit Nehru spoke dramatically at midnight in the Indian Legislative Assembly saying that "*Long years ago we made a tryst with destiny and now the time has come when we shall redeem our pledge, not wholly or in full measure, but very substantially. At the stroke of the midnight hour, while the world sleeps, India will awake to life and freedom.*"[17]

The partition boundaries had been surveyed in advance and drawn up by an independent Boundary Commission, headed by English lawyer Sir Cyril Radcliffe, whose decision all parties agreed to abide by. Pakistan was to consist of the western provinces of Sind, North West Frontier and Baluchistan, and part of the Punjab, as West Pakistan, and a much smaller separate part of the country, a part of Bengal, 1,000 miles to the east, as East Pakistan. There was no linking corridor of land, an arrangement that was to prove an impractical solution. The new India, consisted of the remainder of British India. It sought to become a secular state, embracing all religious interests. Pakistan opted for an Islamic *Muslim* state. India was headed by Jawarlal Pandit Nehru as Prime Minister with the powerful Vallabhai Patel as Home Minister and Minister for States, with Lord Mountbatten staying on at the invitation of India as Governor-General of India until April 1948, later extended to 21st June 1948. Pakistan was headed by Mohammed Ali Jinnah (known by then as '*Quaid-i-Azam*', or the Great Leader), as Governor-General and Liaquat Ali Khan as

Prime Minister, with Karachi as the capital [17,60,84] (See Figs. 8 & 9)

The rulers of the independent Indian Princely States of the former India were permitted to choose between acceding to one or other of the two new nations, or risk remaining independent. There were 565 Princely states by 1947, recognised and respected by the British, varying in size from some as large as France to the smallest of a few hundred acres. Only 108 rulers and 12 representatives of lesser states sat in the Government Chamber of Princes. The understanding was that the new nations they joined would take control of defence, foreign policy and communications only and that the princes remaining rights and priviliges and privy purses would be protected as inviolate.[84] In the event India, to whom the bulk of states were persuaded to join before partition, were to renege on their promises later, and the princes were to lose most of their rights. The states generally joined the adjacent, or surrounding nation with the same religious affiliation as the majority of people in the state. One of the major exceptions was the large and wealthy princely state of Hyderabad, which is the size of France, where the *Muslim* ruler, *Nizam* Mir Osman Ali, opted to 'resume' independent status, against the ardent wishes of a *Hindu* majority. On the pretext of dissatisfaction with the internal and external policies of the state, it was occupied by force by the Indian Army in September 1948, and incorporated into India. Many thousands of *Muslims* were killed and raped before order was restored. There was also the beautiful and equally large state of Kashmir, in the foothills and highlands of the Himalayan mountains, where the Hindu *Maharajah* Sir Hari Singh ignored the aspirations of the majority *Muslims* by opting to join India. But not before Kashmir was invaded by tribesman from the North West Frontier of Pakistan in October 1947. Since when a small part, known as Azad Kashmir, was temporarily occupied, and remains under Pakistan protection, awaiting a United Nations plebiscite on the rightful status of the whole state of Kashmir. This inequitable state of affairs has resulted in constant conflict between the two nations ever since. The small but significant Muslim ruled Junagadh state (Pop. 700,000) in the Gujerat area, also acceded after partition to Pakistan, despite its Hindu majority. Although legitimate, India objected, the Nawab fled and following an invitation by the Junagadh State Council to intervene, India absorbed the state after a dubious understanding between Nehru and Liaqat Ali Khan of Pakistan that the result of plebiscites would be respected (the latter thinking of Kashmir). In the event a plebiscite in Junagadh in February 1948 voted overwhelmingly to remain in India.[84]

Much communal blood letting between the *Hindus* and *Muslims* resulted from the decision to partition the country, and after the act of partition it continued for many months. It resulted in hundreds of thousands of deaths and injured, to both the major Indian communities, and others besides, with the most foul and cruel atrocities on both sides, before begrudging acceptance of the new states, except mainly in Kashmir. Much of the blood letting occurred during the mass migration between the countries of between 6 and 8 million people each way, which preceded and followed partition. It was one of the greatest migrations ever recorded in history. It did little credit to the British nation, who so ably and peacefully governed the former country of India as a British crown colony for nearly 100 years. It had governed 400 million people, with its cocktail of major religious affiliations, including *Hindu, Muslim, Sikh, Buddhist* and Christian, in descending order of size, intermingled, with minimum bloodshed, and yet were unable to devise a workable plan to control its sectarian orientated partition without a major blood bath. Some say that the last Viceroy Lord Louis Mountbatten misjudged the depth of ill feeling between *Hindu* and *Muslim* and that he could have avoided the carnage had he taken the advice given him by Sir Evan Jenkins, Governor of the Punjab, and his Commander-in-Chief General Sir Claude Auchinleck. They advocated more time in the independence process, as at first envisaged, and also to use military force to preserve peace and order throughout.[61] The atrocities near heavily populated Calcutta, where the majority were expected as the *Muslims* fled to East Pakistan, were small compared to the Punjab, due mainly to the efforts of *Mahatma* Gandhi, who was residing near there at the time. A 50,000 strong independent Punjab Boundary Force was created, mostly British officered, to keep the peace there. They consisted of a mixed force of *Gurkha, Hindu* and *Muslim* troops, which latter had divided allegiances, and the force only had limited powers. It was said to have been too small and formed too late, and was a tragic failure, being unable to control the blood letting that ensued. It was disbanded on 29th August 1947.[84] The commander was the British veteran of the Burma campaign Major-General T.W. Rees, whose advisers were Brigadier Ayub Khan (later to become General Ayub Khan the President of Pakistan in 1958) and Brigadier Brar, a *Sikh*.[23,84] Up to half a million natives were said to have perished during partition, with millions injured and 14 million displaced, in a very short space of time. It was the most painful and bloody 'labour,' in the 'conception' of two new great nations. However it did confirm that it was the presence of the British in India during the *Raj*, in both civil and military administration, each of which maintained a mix of India's religions, which ensured stability in the former British India, through a bond of mutual respect and trust, which had built up over time, and still exists between the British and the peoples of the Indian subcontinent. For a time Mountbatten chaired an Emergency Committee with overriding powers to restore order, which impinged on every field of national life in India, from harvesting crops abandoned by refugees to injections against cholera. Order in the Punjab was not restored until early November 1947, when the refugees crossing the border almost ceased.[84]

The old Indian Army was disbanded and the troops, all apart from four regiments of *Gurkhas* who became part of the British Army, were divided between the two new countries of India and Pakistan, as were the Indian Navy and Air Force. The number of Indian Officers in the Indian Army had risen from only a 1,000 or so in 1939 to 15,750 in 1946. 30 Battalions of the British Army in India were repatriated at partition. The last of the British troops, the 1st Battalion Somerset Light Infantry, did not depart for the United Kingdom until 28th February 1948 on the '*Empress of Australia*', after a special ceremony of '*The Escort of the Colours*' beside the '*Gateway of India*' in Bombay.[61] Before the boat sailed, as with tradition the band of the Royal Marines played them off from the quay, and the troops doubtless sang *'Bless 'em all'* (by Jimmy Hughes & Frank Lane);-

' They say there's a troop ship just leaving Bombay,
Bound for Old Blighty shore,
Heavily laden with time expired men,
Bound for the land they adore.' etc

The majority of British *Europeans* and many thousands of *Anglo-Indians*, left the country before partition and soon after, to return *Home*, or to seek new lives in British Commonwealth countries, many after generations spent in India. The Indian Civil Service, and other civilian services and equipment were divided between the two new nations, except for the government printing presses.[84] Some British *Europeans* and *Anglo-Indians*, were asked to stay on to ensure a smooth transfer of power. *' The British government guaranteed compensation and pensions, graded according to length of service, to British officers who would be deprived of their careers......... To these men, India and Pakistan owe much more than they are as yet willing to admit'.*[23] By 1946 some 50 percent of the senior official positions in the I.C.S.were already held by Indians. After independence the countries of India and Pakistan closed their doors to the expertise of British and other expatriate Engineers and consultants, choosing understandably to rely on the considerable fund of well trained, well qualified professionals of their own. This policy began to change quite early in Pakistan, and has reached an openness in both countries since (and in Bangladesh also), which is heartening and can only be beneficial to all parties.

9. Post Independence India and Pakistan -

In 1945 the *Sind-Punjab Agreement* had been signed by the provincial governments of Punjab and Sind to ensure equitable sharing for irrigation of the waters of the Punjab rivers, the Indus, Jhelum, Chenab, Sutlej, Ravi and Beas between the Punjab and the Sind provinces during the British *Raj*. However with the partition of pre-*Raj* India into the two independent countries of India and Pakistan in 1947, it became necessary to arrange more positive physical constraints to this sharing. After years of negotiating the *Indus Waters Treaty* was signed by the two countries in 1960, to be finally implemented by 1970. This allowed India priority use of all the waters of the Ravi, Beas and Sutlej rivers, and Pakistan the same for the River Indus and the Jhelum and Chenab rivers. The requisite dams and Link Canals to effect this were subsequently installed, with the aid of funds from the World Bank, including the great Mangla and Tarbela dams on the Kashmir frontier. Meanwhile to overcome shortages in the Sind, the Ghulam Mohammed Barrage was constructed in 1955 near Hyderabad, and in 1961 the Gudu Barrage, near Kashmore,100 miles and 350 miles respectively north of Karachi. The increased application of irrigation water in the Sind, after the British left India, resulted in wide spread waterlogging and attendant salinity in the irrigated tracts, causing severe damage to the soil and severely reducing crop output. A contributing factor had been the

British failure to install adequate land drains in the Sukkur Barrage command. British Consulting Engineers and Agricultural experts were called in by the Pakistan Government in 1961 to report on the matter. The resulting Lower Indus Report on which I was engaged, which was submitted to the Pakistan Government five years later in 1966, recommended massive remodelling of the whole Sind irrigation systems, with the introduction of land drainage throughout. This gigantic project, which is the largest of its kind in the world, covers an area equal to the size of England, and is currently still under construction (see Appendix 4).

In the 1951 Census the population of India was given as nearly 357 million, and Pakistan had nearly 76 million, including about 42 million in East Pakistan, which later became Bangladesh in 1971. A further 4 million people lived in disputed Kashmir and about half a million in the disputed Assam Tribal Areas. The 1961 census gave the population of India as approximately 435.5 million people, of which percentages by religion were given as *Hindu* (c.85%), *Muslim* (c.10%), Christian (c.2%), *Sikh* (c.2%), *Jain, Buddhist, Parsi,* Jewish etc. (c.1%). The 1961 census of Pakistan gave the population as West Pakistan 43 million, East Pakistan (later Bangladesh) approximately 51 million. The religious division was not given, but that for 1951 was *Muslim* (c.85.5%), *Hindu* (c.12.9%), Christian (0.7%)*Buddhist, Parsee* etc. (c.0.9%).[26]

Less than six months after the declaration of independence for India and Pakistan, the nationally and internationally revered figure of *Mahatma* Gandhi, who spent his life expounding the virtues of peace and non-violence, and who was most responsible for the departure of the British from the Indian sub-continent, was no more. He was assassinated at a prayer meeting in *Birla House* in Delhi on 30th January 1948 by an Indian *Hindu Brahmin* extremist from Poona, who objected to his teachings of tolerance, amidst cries of '*Mahatma Gandhi ke jai*' (Hail Mahatma Gandhi) and '*Gandhiji amar ho gaye*' (Gandhiji has become immortal). Barely eight months later Mohammed Ali Jinnah the founder of Pakistan, died of a heart attack in September 1948. He was succeeded by Khwaja Nazimuddin, who subsequently became Prime Minister at the death of Liaquat Ali Khan, who was assassinated in October 1951, by one of his countrymen, allegedly for his moderate attitude towards India. The new Governor-General of Pakistan, Ghulam Mohammed, an ambitious man who replaced Nazimudin in 1953 with Mohammed Ali of Bogra, was in turn replaced by Major General Iskander Mirza in 1955, the first military leader of the country. Chaudhuri Mohammed Ali became Prime Minister of Pakistan in 1956, followed in short order by H.S. Suhrawardy in 1957, I.I.Chundrigar the same year, followed by the respected Malik Firoz Khan Noon, who proved unable to arrest the decline in domestic conditions.

India became a sovereign democratic Republic within the Commonwealth in 1950 with Rajendra Prasad as the first President, a constitutional rather than an executive function, shared over the years by both *Hindu* and *Muslim* appointments, but with power remaining always in the hands of the Prime Minister. Pakistan also became a Republic within the Commonwealth in 1956, with Major General Iskander Mirza as the first President of the Republic. He was replaced by the Commander in Chief of the army General Mohammed Ayub Khan in 1958, when martial law was declared to avoid bloody revolution from a catalogue of popular grievances. He moved the capital to Rawalpindi, before installing it in the specially built town of Islamabad nearby. In 1959 the Chinese occupied the Ladakh portion of Kashmir. The Indian Prime Minister Pandit Nehru passed away in 1964, and was succeeded by Lal Bahadur Shastri until his premature death in 1966, when he was succeeded by Nehru's daughter Indira Priyadarshini Gandhi, who survived the next eleven years in power. She returned to power in 1980, having been first succeeded by Morarji Desai in 1977, followed by Charan Singh in early 1980. She was assassinated, by her own *Sikh* bodyguard in 1984, in retribution for the the attack of the holy shrine of the *Sikhs*, the Golden Temple at Amritsar. Her son Rajib Gandhi, who succeeded her, was also assassinated by a Sri Lankan separatist in 1991, marking the end of the Nehru dynasty. V.P. Singh, P.M. in 1989, was replaced by Chandra Shekar for trying to reserve government posts for *dalits (Untouchables)*. He was followed by Narasimha Rao and in 1996 H.D. Deve Gowda. In 1997 K.R. Narayan from Kerala was the first *dalit* to be elected President. The *Congress Party* were routed in 1998 by a coalition headed by the extreme right Hindu nationalist *Bharatiya Janata Party* (B.J.P.), whose leader Atal Bihari Vajpayee became Prime Minister. They are the politcal arm of the *Rashtriya Swayamsewak Sangh* (R.S.S.) the Hindu fundamentalist group, who are causing conflicts with the very large Muslim minority and persecution of the very small Christian minority in India. In year 2000 the opposition *Congress Party* was led unsuccessfully in elections by Sonia Gandhi, the Italian born widow of assasinated Rajib Gandhi.

Indo-Pakistan border incidents have continued over the years in Kashmir, following the Pakistani tribal incursion in 1947, culminating in September 1965 in the Pakistan Army forces entering Indian controlled Kashmir. India responded by moving Indian troops towards Lahore, and Hyderabad in Sind. A ceasefire was declared fortuitously only three weeks later, following intervention by the United Nations.[26] I was engaged in Civil Engineering work in the Sind at the time, and a hundred of us expatriate experts and families were forced evacuate to Karachi, with women and children onward to England, after parachute raids by the Indians north of Karachi were reported. The situation has remained tense between the two countries ever since, a sensitivity which became evident during the visit of Queen Elizabeth II to India and Pakistan in 1997, when references to the need to resolve the Kashmir affair by the British were repulsed, as interference in internal affairs.

During the Pakistan presidency of General Aga Mohammed Yahya Khan, who succeeded Field Marshal Ayub Khan in 1969, East Pakistan declared itself as the independent state of Bangladesh in 1971. It followed the summary arrest of the chief of the *Awami League Party*, Sheik Mujibir Rahman, who was set on self government, and who won all but two seats in the East Pakistan elections. Months of guerrilla activity followed, supported by Pakistan armed forces loyal to the Bengali movement, which resulted in much bloodshed and in 10 million people fleeing to India. The Pakistan Army were ultimately defeated by the combined forces of the *Mukti Bahini* guerrillas, of which there were some 100,000, aided by the Indian Army, in a war lasting only 13 days. Yahya Khan was forced to resign in favour of Zulfikar Ali Bhutto, a civilian and son of a rich Sindhi landowner. He released Sheik Mujib from internment to become the first Prime Minister of the new republic of Bangladesh ('The Land of Bengal') with its capital at Dacca (*Dhaka*); the last division of what was once the great British Indian Empire.

Abu Sayeed Choudhury became the first President of Bangladesh. In 1972 Bangladesh became a member of the Commonwealth. The same year Pakistan left the Commonwealth. Bhutto (who I once met in the Sind in 1962), ended Martial Law, and Pakistan and India signed an agreement to withdraw military forces from the borders of their countries 26,61 (see Figure 10). Following unrest Sheik Mujib assumed the Presidency of Bangladesh in early 1975. Seven months later he and his family were assassinated by army officers for favouritism and corruption, and this country, one of the poorest and most populous countries in the world has moved from crisis to crisis ever since. Major General Zia ur Rahim came into power but was also assassinated in 1981 by the military. Civilian vice-President Abdus Sattar became President in 1982, but was ejected by Lieut. General Hussein Mohammed Ershad, who took over as chief martial law administrator in 1983. He was successful in the 1986 election and after retiring from the army in 1987 received 87% of the vote for President, when Mujib's daughter Sheik Hasina Wajad and Begum Kaleda Zia ur Rahim, wife of the slain former President boycotted the election. A poor state of the economy and weeks of violent demonstrations forced Ershad to resign in 1990. In early 1991 the *Bangladesh Nationalist Party* (B.N.P.) won parliamentary elections and Kaleda Zia became P.M. Ershad was imprisoned for corruption and arms offences. Following political unrest in 1995 President Abdur Rahman Biswas dissolved Parliament. In 1996 Shabuddin Ahmed became President and Sheik ur Rahman of the *Awami Leaque* (A.L.) became P.M. India and Bangladesh signed treaties in 1996 and 1997 to share the waters of their common rivers the Ganges and the Teesta respectively. Repeated cyclonic flooding and tidal waves in the vast Ganges delta region and the South east have been the constant scourge of the nation. Despite costly new flood defences in 1994, following 130,000 deaths in 1991, many continue to perish most years and many thousands are made homeless in this unfortunate and forgotten land. Only the urban centres Dacca and Chittagong see any development.

In Pakistan, Bhutto introduced a new Islamic Constitution in Pakistan and in 1973 reverted to Prime Minister. His party the *People's Party of Pakistan* (P.P.P.) were accused of rigging the elections they won in 1977, and as a consequence the Army Commander-in-Chief General Mohammed Zia-ul-Haq seized power in a bloodless coup in 1978. Mr Bhutto was sentenced to death for 'political murder', for which he was executed in April 1979. Zia-ul-Haq became President assuming absolute power, and martial law was reinstituted. Pakistan began manufacturing nuclear weapons, as

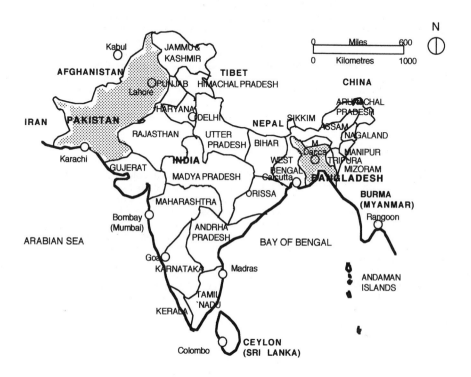

N

| | Miles | 600 |
| 0 | Kilometres | 1000 |

Kabul
JAMMU &
KASHMIR
AFGHANISTAN
TIBET
CHINA
PUNJAB HIMACHAL PRADESH
Lahore
ARUNACHAL
PRADESH
HARYANA
DELHI
NEPAL SIKKIM
ASSAM
IRAN PAKISTAN
NAGALAND
RAJASTHAN
UTTER
PRADESH BIHAR
M
Dacca
MANIPUR
Karachi
INDIA
WEST
TRIPURA
GUJERAT
BENGAL
MIZORAM
MADYA PRADESH
Calcutta BANGLADESH
ORISSA
BURMA
(MYANMAR)
MAHARASHTRA
Rangoon
Bombay
(Mumbai)
ANDRHA
PRADESH
ARABIAN SEA
BAY OF BENGAL
Goa
KARNATAKA
ANDAMAN
ISLANDS
Madras
TAMIL
NADU
KERALA

CEYLON
Colombo
(SRI LANKA)

Figure 10:
INDIA, PAKISTAN & BANGLADESH IN 1995

Legend: M = Meghalaya

had India in 1974, increasing border tensions between the two countries. Following pressure from the people over a period of years for democracy, so called non-party elections for a National Assembly were held in 1985, and Mohammed Khan Juneju was made Prime Minister, with Zia-ul-Haq remaining President. President Zia-ul-Haq was killed in a mid-air plane explosion in 1988. Pakistan rejoined the Commonwealth in 1989. Benazir Bhutto, daughter of Zulfikar Ali Bhutto, became Prime Minister, only to be dismissed in 1990, as was her successor Nawaz Sharif in 1993. Benazir Bhutto returned to power, but was again dismissed on corruption charges in 1997 by the President Farooq Leghari. Nawaz Sharif was once again elected Prime Minister. He was again ousted by General Pervaiz Musharraf in a bloodless coup in October 1999, and held on charges of treason, hijacking and attempted murder. He was given life imprisonment in 2000. Musharraf, allededly plans to hold democratic elections, overseen by the current President Rafiq Tarar and nervously awaited by India and the western world.

10. Ceylon Independence 1948 -

Ceylon (*Sri Lanka*) which had become a Crown colony in 1802 was given independence from the *Raj* in February 1948, with D.S. Senanayake the first Prime Minister of a Westminster style government, and Lord Soulbury as Governor General. Following a fatal riding accident in 1951 he was succeeded by his son Dudley for a short while before Sir John Kotelawala became Prime Minister. In 1954 Sir Oliver Gometilleke, the Finance Minister, was appointed Governor General. In the 1956 General Election Kotelawala's *United Nationalist's Party* (U.N.P.) was toppled by the *Sri Lanka Freedom Party* (S.L.F.P.) of S.W.R.D. Bandaranaike. However he alienated the *Tamil* minority of the country by making *Sinhalese* the sole official language, and by taking measures to state support *Buddhism* and the *Sinhala* culture. As a result the country has suffered persistent sectarian terrorism from the '*Tamil Tigers*' until the present day. Bandaranaike was assassinated in 1959 and Dudley Senanayake returned again as P.M. for a short while before being replaced by Sirimavo Bandaranaike, the widow of the former Prime Minister in 1960. She proceeded to Nationalise church schools, insurance, oil and petrol import and distribution and imposed stiff control over foreign banks and export firms, to control economic drift. Her husband had already nationalised bus transport and the port of Colombo. Mrs Bandaranaike was supplanted by Senanayake in 1965, but she was returned in 1970. A rebellion in 1971, which necessitated the declaration of a state of emergency, was crushed with military equipment assistance provided by the United Kingdom, India and the U.S.S.R. In May 1972 Ceylon proclaimed itself a socialist republic, taking its ancient name of *Sri Lanka*, but remaining within the Commonwealth. Mrs Banderanaike remained as Prime Minister and William Gopallawa, the former Governor General, was made the first President.

In 1977 Junius Richard Jayawardene of the U.N.P. swept into power, but *Tamil-Sinhalese* violence erupted threatening relations with India. Although this was deftly resolved *Tamil* separatism remained. In 1978

J.R.Jayawardene became President and Ranasingle Premadesa P.M. The economy improved at first and in 1981 foreign investment was welcomed, but without success. Emergency powers had to be used to quell communal violence. In 1982 a new parliamentary capital 5 miles south of Colombo, was named Jayavardhanapura Kotte, in honour of the President. Following *Sinhalese* militancy against the *Tamils* in 1987, the latter were offered an autonomous province in the north east within a united *Sri Lanka*, with an Indian Peace Keeping Force (I.P.K.F.) to enforce terms. The *Liberation Tigers of Tamil Eelam* (L.T.T.E.), the political arm of the *Tamil Tigers*, disagreed over implementation. Jayawardene was succeeded by Premadasa in 1989, the I.P.K.F. withdrew and *Tamil* terrorism was resumed. Premadasa was assassinated by *Tamils* in 1993 and Dingiri Banda Wigetunga replaced him as President, with *Tamil* terrorism his greatest challenge. Ranil Wickremansinghe was made P.M. and with some success. In 1994 Chandrika Kumaratunga of the *People's Alliance* became P.M. and the opposition leader Gavnini Dissanayake was assassinated despite efforts to negotiate with the *Tamil Tigers*. A 1995 truce with L.T.T.E was short lived. The Government offensive intensified and Jaffna and the peninsula were captured. In 1996 Kumaratunga was President assisted by the dynastic Sirimavo Bandaranaike as P.M. In 1997 the Government offered to discuss autonomy again with both the *Tamils* and *Muslims*, with whom trouble had also erupted, but without success and the problem continues until this day.

11. Burma Independence 1948 -

In Burma, after the Japanese occupied the country in 1942 they set up a Civil Administration under Ba Maw, and on 1st August 1943 Burma was declared an independent state. On the eve of the Japanese defeat in 1945 Thakin Aung San, the Defence chief, heading a new political party called the *Anti-Fascist People's Freedom League* (A.F.P.F.L.), successfully demanded independence of the British Labour Government. However before it was formally granted he was assassinated. The independent *Republic of the Union of Burma* came into existence on 4th January 1948, with U Nu the former Foreign Affairs Minister as Prime Minister and head of state. A year later it left the Commonwealth. After briefly handing over to U Ba Swe in 1956 U Nu resumed Premiership in 1957, but resigned in 1958 in favour of General U Ne Win who promised to restore internal order. U Nu resumed premiership again after the 1960 general election only to have it overturned by U Ne Win, with the assistance of the army in 1962. U Ne Win's anti-communist *Revolutionary Council* one party government stayed in power until 1972, when he resigned his army commission and became Chairman of the State Council (President) and Prime Minister of the first civilian government in 10 years. In 1974 U Sein Win became Prime Minister and was succeeded by U Maung Maung Kha in 1977. U Ne Win remained Chairman of the State Council until 1984 when he was succeeded by U San Yu. In 1988 a military junta seized power, refusing to recognise the democratically elected Aung San Suu Kyi. The country was renamed *Myanmar* in 1989. Popular resistance to the oppressive regime of the junta continues to this day.

APPENDIX 1

GOVERNORS GENERAL AND VICEROYS OF BRITISH INDIA

'The future Viceroy must...not be guided by the
snobbish and vulgar, over-bearing and offensive
behaviour of our Civil and Political Agents, if we are
to go on peaceably and happily in India...not trying
to trample on the people and continuously reminding
them and making them feel they are a conquered people.'

(Letter to Lord Salisbury, 27 May 1898
in *'Superior Person'* by Kenneth Rose 1969)

VISCOUNT MERSEY IN HIS ADMIRABLE BOOK *'The Viceroys and Governors General of India'*[1] lists 33 Governors General and Viceroys of India during the British *Raj*, and Lord Clive designated only Governor of Bengal. Of these 6 were Scots, 6 were Irish and the remaining 22, including the naturalised Lord Mountbatten, were English. *'Most Viceroys were active and industrious men from their youth up. The Scots were perhaps more distinguished for their application and tenacity, the Irish for their lighter hands and strokes of genius.'* [1] The title of Governor General only commenced in 1774 with Warren Hastings. From 1858 the title of Viceroy, or royal ruler of India, in the absence of the King Emperor, was added (though not in the patent), although the latter name was commonly used during the *Raj*.

Governors of Bengal

1758-1760 & 1765-1767 Robert Clive, Lord Clive of Plassey
1772-1774 Warren Hastings

Governors General

1774-1785 Warren Hastings
1786-1793 Charles Marquess Cornwallis
1793-1798 Sir John Shore, Lord Teignmouth
1798-1805 Richard Marquess Wellesley, Earl of Mornington,
1805-1807 Charles Marquess Cornwallis (2nd time)
1807-1813 Gilbert Elliot, Earl of Minto
1814-1823 Francis Rawdon, Marquess of Hastings, Earl of Moira
1823-1828 William Pitt, Earl Amherst
1828-1835 Lord William Cavendish Bentinck
1835-1842 George Eden, Earl of Auckland
1842-1844 Edward Law, Earl Ellenborough
1844-1848 Henry Viscount Hardinge
1848-1856 James Andrew Broun-Ramsay, Marquess of Dalhousie
1856-1858 Charles John Canning, Earl Canning

Governors General & Viceroys

1858-1862 Charles John Canning, Earl Canning
1862-1863 James Bruce, Earl of Elgin
1863-1869 John Laird Mair Lawrence, Lord Lawrence of the Punjab
1869-1872 Richard Bourke, Earl of Mayo
1872-1876 Thomas Baring, Earl of Northbrook
1876-1880 Edward Robert Bulwer, Earl of Lytton
1880-1884 George Frederick Robinson, Marquess of Ripon
1884-1888 Frederick Hamilton-Temple-Blackwood, Marquess of
          Dufferin
1888-1894 Henry Charles Petty-Fitzmaurice, Marquess of Lansdowne
1894-1899 Victor Alexander Bruce, Earl of Elgin
1899-1905 George Nathaniel Curzon, Marquess Curzon
1905-1910 Gilbert John Elliot, Earl of Minto
1910-1916 Charles Hardinge, Lord Hardinge of Penshurst
1916-1921 Frederick John Thesiger, Viscount Chelmsford
1921-1926 Rufus Isaacs, Marquess of Reading
1926-1931 Edward Frederick Lindley Wood, Lord Irwin, Earl Halifax
1931-1936 Freeman Freeman-Thomas, Marquess of Willingdon
1936-1943 Victor Alexander John Hope, Marquess of Linlithgow
1943-1947 Archibald Percival Wavell, Earl Wavell
1947 (April to August) Admiral Louis Francis Victor Albert
          Mountbatten, Earl Mountbatten of Burma

APPENDIX 2

ANGLO-INDIAN SCHOOLS

It's Army School for you my boy.
Nai, nai, kubi nai.
Ayah can't teach you any more,
Nai, nai, kubi nai.
It's off to public school my boy,
Nai, nai, kubi nai.
Kirkee can't teach you any more,
Nai, nai, kubi nai.
Bangalore School's too far my boy,
Nai, nai, kubi nai.
Off to Deolali for you my boy,
Nai, nai, kubi nai.
Japs are coming soon my boy,
Nai, nai, kubi nai.
Back to Poona for you my boy,
Nai, nai, kubi nai.
Now the war is over my boy,
Nai, nai, kubi nai.
Off to England for you my boy,
Nai, nai, kubi nai.

(*' Eschul Chulloa Chotah Sahib'*
(Go to School Young Sir)
by Alfred D.F.(George) Gabb 1997)

CONTRARY TO THE IMPRESSION given in literature, of the 300,000 *Europeans*, and *Anglo-Indians* in India in the 1931 Census, the majority of children probably did not return to England for their education, nor did they otherwise all attend schools in the foothills of the Himalayas. Most attended schools in the hot Indo-Gangetic plains and the Deccan plateau of central India, as the following will show.

The Christian Church played an enormous part in the provision of schools for both *Domiciled Europeans* and *Anglo-Indians* in India, with the considerable and much beloved efforts of the dedicated clergy and nuns of the Roman Catholic and Anglican religious Orders, not to mention the Methodist, Quakers and other denominations also. Their excellent missionary schools, colleges and convents, which spread across the country, stood, and still stand as testimony to their dedication and success. As do those schools installed by the great efforts of the Church Missionary Society (C.M.S.), Foreign Missions Society (F.M.S.), Society for the Promotion of Christian Knowledge (S.P.C.K.), the London Missionary Society (L.M.S.) and the early clergy of the East India Company. These pioneers also opened remarkably successful schools for Indians too, of whatever creed, be it *Hindu, Muslim, Buddhist,* or Christian, with a brand of muscular social and academic education, based on Christian ideals of

89

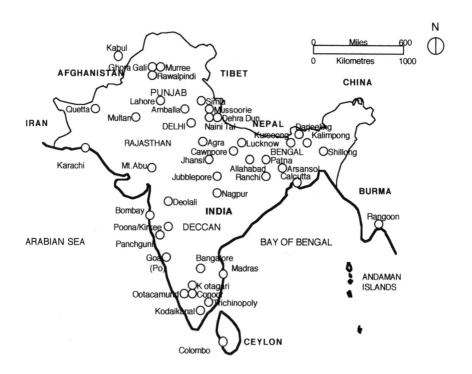

Figure 11:
BRITISH RAJ ANGLO-INDIAN SCHOOLS

behaviour, until then alien to the Indians; an impressive achievement, considering then bigotry of the Indian religions and class systems.[34] In 1784 the S.P.C.K. reported

> '...a considerable number of children born annually in British settlements in the East Indies of fathers who are European and mothers who are natives.......seven hundred at Madras......the fathers .....being usually soldiers, sailors, and the lower order of people too often neglect their offspring and suffer them to follow the caste of their mothers.....'

The S.P.C.K. and other Christian societies then received no financial aid from the E.I.C. for the schooling of these children, then known as Eurasian, but had to rely on their own resources.[1,2,26]

Many private elementary schools first sprang up in the country, especially for poor and underprivileged children, dating from the earliest called Pringle's, in Madras (Chennai) in 1673, started by a Scottish preacher of that name, brought out by the E.I.C. as Headmaster. The Reverend Richard Cobbe, a Church of England Chaplain to the E.I.C., founded in 1718 a small free school for poor boys in the Fort area of Bombay (Mumbai). Later in 1815 a subsequent Company Chaplain, Archdeacon George Barnes, formed the Bombay Education Society (B.E.S.), which took over the old school, and with the aid of land gifted by the Government, opened a new school, Christ Church School, a day school for boys and girls, in 1825 in Byculla, Bombay. The B.E.S. schools were primarily meant for poor Europeans and their progeny the Anglo-Indian children, whose numbers were steadily increasing. The B.E.S. amalgamated in the early 1920s with the Indo-British Institution, which had been founded by the Reverend George Candy in about 1837. As Christ Church School was becoming overcrowded, the B.E.S., with plans initiated by Sir Reginald Spence and Mr Haig-Brown, members of the Board of Governors, purchased 250 acres of land near the village of Deolali (Devlali), 150 miles inland on the elevated Deccan plateau, which provided a healthier climate than Bombay, and there built Barnes High School, a co-educational boarding school, which was opened in 1925. It was a modern school, well ahead of its time. It was the largest boarding school in west India, and one of the largest in the whole of India. The foundation stone was laid by Sir George Lloyd, later Governor of Bombay Presidency. The first Principal of Barnes School was the Rev. Thomas Evans until 1934, when he was succeeded by his deputy W.R. Coles, who was the last Principal during the Raj. In 1946 the school had about 350 pupils, consisting mainly of Anglo-Indians, with a few Domiciled Europeans and a handful of Indians, Parsies, Iranians and Burmese. The Barnes school teachers were a mix of Domiciled Europeans and Anglo-Indians.[6]   Both schools still survive, with many charitable placements, and continue to provide a high class of education. W.R. Coles retired in 1969 to be replaced by J.L. Davis, who was himself succeeded by Alan Baker, the present Principal of Barnes School in 1985. My two sisters, elder brother and I and two of my maternal cousins attended Barnes School as boarders between 1940 and 1946. My elder sister was Head Girl in 1942. We had been moved

Barnes High School, Deolali (*Devlali*) in 1945 -
(Copy of a school Christmas card, with a print of a painting by Art Master
Fenton Bailey; with acknowledgements to the Principal, Barnes School).

Barnes High School, Deolali (*Devlali*) -
Administration Block in 1995

there to be closer to home than our earlier school in Bangalore, during the Second World War. I was kindly put up in the guest house by the amiable Principal, and given the freedom of the school, when I visited India in 1995. I found the present teaching staff consists of *Anglo-Indians* and Indians, with the Principal being a *Domiciled European*. Of the present 1150 pupils, 550 of which are day scholars, the majority appear now to be Indian, and the remainder *Anglo-Indian*. The school premises have been enlarged with the addition of a Junior Academy in 1977. The old swimming pool, fondly known in my time as the 'duck's pond' was destroyed in an earthquake in 1994 and the Principal is raising funds from donations towards a new one, and also for a new Christian Chapel independent of the Administration block.[12] The *Besian Society*, which represents the old boys and girls of Barnes and Christ Church Schools, has an annual reunion in south London each September. Sheila O'Connor is the friendly Secretary, and can be contacted at 36 Netherhouse Moor, Church Crookham, Fleet. Hampshire GU13 OTY (Tel (01252)613346. In India also, old boys and girls meet once a year in October at the school, to share their experiences and engage in sport, and I was able to enjoy meeting some of them. The school address is Barnes School, (*Bombay Education Society*), Devlali - 422 401, Nasik District, Maharashtra, India, Tel. No. 0253 41253.

In 1731 in Calcutta *(Kolkata)*, what became known as the Calcutta Free Schools were started. Major William Kirkpatrick later founded the Upper and Lower Military Orphanages in Calcutta also in 1782, followed by similar institutions in Madras *(Chennai)*, founded by Lady Campbell, the wife of the Governor of Madras. Children of the E.I.C. and Royal armies were sent to orphanages, especially if born of a liaison with an Indian or *Anglo-Indian* woman. Children of officers were cared for in separate institutions and enjoyed a better education than the children of B.O.R.s. Boys in the latter mostly became non-combatants in the army in their early teens, mostly as bandsmen. The former and brighter boys joined the uncovenanted civil service, or were trained as surveyors, mechanical engineers or apothecaries. The girls in orphanages were taught to become good wives, with lessons in needlework, music and dancing. They became wives often in their early teens.[15] In 1820 there were several other private schools in Calcutta, such as Archer's School, Ardwise's Academy, Drummond's Academy and Farrell's Seminary.[28]

Further great strides were made in the 19th century to improve the education available to *Anglo-Indian* and *Domiciled European* girls and boys in India, by their own efforts principally, both military and civilian, charitable and fee paying, private and government. John Ricketts, a leader in the *Anglo-Indian Community* in Calcutta, in his endeavour to provide mechanical and agricultural craft training founded the Calcutta Apprenticing Society and Marine School, with limited success. This he followed with the Calcutta Commercial and Patriotic Association in 1827, for similar training, which although generously supported by the Governor of Bombay Sir John Malcolm, with land at the Phoolshair Colony near Poona, failed shortly after, due to the *'moral turpitude'* of the schoolmaster.[28]. Before this in 1823 Ricketts was instrumental in forming the successful Parental Academic Institution in Calcutta, which following a large legacy from the *Anglo-Indian* Captain   John Doveton [15], became the Doveton College. This later became the Calcutta Grammar School, and ultimately the prestigious St. Paul's School, now in Darjeeling, in the lower Himalayas north of Calcutta. The prestigious La Martinière Colleges at Calcutta (1836) and Lucknow (1840), were spawned at this time, the latter in the former palatial residence of the French military adventurer and E.I.C. Major-General Claude Martine, who had bequeathed both schools for *European* and *Anglo-Indian* children. During the Indian Mutiny of 1857-59 pupils from La Martinière College, Lucknow, actually assisted the military in the defence of the British Residency against the mutineers. In recognition of this the school was belatedly awarded Battle Honours in 1932. It is the only school in the world to be so honoured.[19] The children also received Indian Mutiny Medals with Defence of Lucknow inscribed on them.[16] My father passed out of the college in 1917. The current Principal of Barnes School, Alan Baker, an Old Martinian, was able to assure me in 1995 that the colleges still survive, and continue to give a high class of education on the British pattern. The Old Martinians Association can be contacted c/o the Secretary J.S.Kaul, Old Martinians Association, 5 China Bazaar, Lucknow - 226 001 India Tel. 233083. The School address is La Martinère College, Dilkusha, Lucknow 226001, Uttar Pradesh, India.

Also started was St. Xavier's College, Calcutta (1834) and Madras Grammar School, founded by Bishop Corrie (1834).   Many others followed elsewhere, such as Cathedral Grammar School, Bombay (1860), attended by a paternal cousin of mine, and Baldwins (1880), in Bangalore. Anglican Bishop Cotton was a vigorous founder of schools, and was an active campaigner in persuading the government through Lord Canning, the first Viceroy of India, to make grants available, and with some success, until he died and Lord Canning was replaced. However it appears that the schools in the hills described so admirably by Hazel Innes Craig in her excellent, and highly recommended book *'Under The Old School Topee'*,[7] primarily may have fared better from this initiative, than the schools in the plains destined mostly for the less privileged *Anglo-Indians*. She lists addresses for Old Boys and Old Girls associations and reunions. Bishop Cotton Schools were opened in Nagpur (1863), Bangalore (1880), and many other locations.

Also in Bangalore the Roman Catholic St Joseph's College (of which St Joseph's *European* Boy's High School was part), though originally conceived in 1841, was first opened by Dr Charbonnaux of the Foreign Missions Society of Paris, France, for *European* boarders, in 1858 in St Joseph's Seminary, built by Rev. Fr. Bouteloup in 1854 in St John's Hill. It also had an orphanage, which was separated from it in 1875. In 1882 Rev. Fr. Vissac, the Rector, affiliated St Joseph's to Madras University and renamed the seminary St Joseph's College, in a bid to make the college one of the leading *European* Colleges in south India. After initially rebuilding the old seminary Father Vissac built a new college on Museum Street in the cantonment, which was opened in 1898. He was followed as Rector in 1902 by Rev. Fr. Froger, and in 1913 by Rev. Fr. Schmitt, a German, who was forced to leave in 1916 because of the war with Germany. Rev. Fr. Leo

St. Joseph's College, Bangalore in 1930's -
(with acknowledgements to the Rector, St.Joseph's Boys High School)

St. Joseph's College, Bangalore - III Field Football Team in 1938 -
with my brother Patrick Gabb third from left in rear & Mr Lynch,
Sports Master

Vanpreene became Rector and Principal in 1916, followed by Rev. Fr. H. Prouvest in 1926. Rev. Fr. R. Collart in 1931 was the last before the College was handed over to the *Society of Jesus* (Jesuits) in 1937, who have run the college ever since. Their first Rector and Principal was Rev. Fr. L. Prosperpio S.J., followed in 1938 by Rev. Fr. Victor Lambert S.J., Rev. Fr. V. Chilardi S.J. and Rev. Fr. C. Studerus S.J. in 1940 and Rev. Fr. E. Jacques until Indian Independence in 1947. The school still survives, and continues to give a high class of education on the British pattern. It is now known as St.Joseph's Boys' High School. The current Rector is Rev. Fr. Ronnie Prabhuand S.J. and the Principal Rev. Fr. Michael John S.J. [13,17,23,24,25,30,31,33] I ran out of time during my visit to India in 1995, as I was run over by a motor scooter, so I was unable to visit this my first boarding school, which I attended from the age of 6 years with my elder brother in 1937, until 1939 when the British declared war on Germany. I was in class in St Anthony's kindergarton school, which was run by the nuns of Good Shepherd Convent, at first. However I was able to correspond with the Rector, who had the Old Boys Association send me particulars of the school today. The *St Joseph's Old Boys Association* (O.B.A.) United Kingdom is very active, meets socially several times annually and produces an excellent journal twice a year.[32] The Secretary's address is Mr U.V. Paul, 28 Alum Close, Holbury, Southampton U.K. SO45 2GY. Tel. (01703) 898479. The old boys also meet annually in September at the school for four days of yarn swapping and sporting activity. The School and O.B.A. address is Rev. Father Michael John S.J., The Principal, St.Joseph's Boys High School, P.O.Box 5031, Museum Road, Bangalore - 560 001, India.

Many other boarding schools in the cooler hill stations began also at this time, such as at Mount Abu in central India, Ootacamund in the Nilgiri Hills, and Simla (*Shimla*), Mussoorie, Naini-Tal, Darjeeling in the Himalayan foothills, and St. Denys, Murree, attended by a cousin of mine. Sir Henry Lawrence, the distinguished soldier and administrator, who was born in Ceylon, founded the first Lawrence Military School in 1846 near Kasauli, in the Simla Hills, and another at Mt. Abu. These were followed after his death by schools at Ootacamund (1858) and Murree (1860), all of which catered for children of British soldiers.[7] Other hill schools opened in Panchgani in the Western Ghats between Bombay and Poona (*Pune*). Three of my maternal cousins attended St. Peter's and Kimmons School there.

The British were also responsible for the impressive Shri Shivaji Preparatory Military School at Bhamburda, a Poona suburb. The school was built as a memorial to Shivaji, the founder of the *Maratha* Empire in the 17th century. The foundation stone was laid by the Prince of Wales in 1922. It was established in 1932, primarily to prepare students for the Indian Military Academy, and military academies in Britain.[32] Its intake was mostly Indian, but there were a sprinkling of *Anglo-Indians* and *Domiciled Europeans* like myself. I attended the school for a short while with my brother at the beginning of 1943, during the Second World War, when a successful invasion of India by the Japanese was feared, and my parents felt a school even nearer my home in Kirkee (*Khadki*), near Poona seemed wise. I am pleased to say this school was still up and running when I visited

Poona in 1995.

A Government *'Report on the Existing Schools for Europeans and Eurasians'* in 1873 concluded that *'the system did not serve the needs of the poorer children of the community'*. This was followed in 1883 by the *'Bengal Code for European Schools'*, by which liberal state aid became available for schools. This applied principally to Bengal, United Provinces, Punjab and Central Provinces. Bombay and Madras were excluded as they already made adequate provision for the education of *Europeans* and *Eurasians*. In 1905 Lord Curzon, the Viceroy of India, instituted the revised *'European Schools' Code'*, to cover all the provinces of British India, including Bombay, Madras and Burma. The *'Seventh Quinquenial Report on Education (1912 - 1917)'* states that there were only seven colleges providing *European* education beyond high school, which were St Joseph's College and College of the Sacred Heart (Bangalore), Woodstock College (Mussoorie), All Saints Diocesan College (Naini Tal) and the *European* Girl's High School (Allahabad). There were also the Teacher's Training College at Sanwar for men and St. Bede's College for women in Simla. There was no special provision of universities for *Europeans* and *Anglo-Indians*. They were required to resort to the Indian universities.[1]

In the 1930s there was much pressure to scrap the *Cambridge School Certificate* in favour of the *Matriculation*, but without success, as the former was considered essential for English university entry. Later attempts were made to Indianise *European* and *Anglo-Indian* school curriculims by introducing Indian history and languages as mandatory. By now the government Education Minister was an Indian, but teaching however remained predominantly *European* until Indian Independence in 1947.

All these schools provided a standard of education, discipline and care comparable to public schools in England during the *Raj*, and had both boarding and day pupil facilities, providing a viable alternative to sending children home to England for education, and at far less cost. Some schools were co-educational, La Martinière, Lucknow being one of the first to open a girl's school in 1869.[20] Hard work and a healthy outdoor life style were encouraged. A great deal of sporting activities in the way of athletics, ball games such as hockey, cricket and football, and even base ball during World War II. Swimming and boxing were also engaged in and made compulsory in most schools, with points awarded to each School House also, to develop the principle of competition to the full. This work and sport ethic was in consequence carried over into adult life, and it was quite common for the *Europeans* and *Anglo-Indians* in India to enjoy a very active sporting life in adulthood, after a hard days work, and not just as spectators, but as participants. Children were of parents from all walks of life, and the schools provided education suitable for the Indian Army, Air Force, Navy, Railways, Post and Telegraph, Customs and Excise, Public Works Department (P.W.D.), Irrigation Department, Medical Services, Forestry Department, Police Department, Civil Service etc. The schools taught, and still continue to teach in English. All had *European* Head Masters and *European* or *Anglo-Indian* teachers, almost exclusively before Indian

94

Independence, except for the teaching of *Urdu* or *Hindi*, the major Indian languages taught as a second language, who were nearly always English speaking *munshis* (Indian teachers).

Although these *Anglo-Indian* schools were basically Christian and intended for *Domiciled Europeans* and *Anglo-Indian* children, they often welcomed a minority of the more wealthy or privileged Indians or Burmese, and also pupils of other religious faiths. The children were not however forced to convert to Christianity, nor to attend formal Sunday religious services. Daily services however, which were almost by way of an 'assembly,' were compulsory and enjoyed by all. These latter entries only remained a minority until Independence in 1947, when the schools were forced to increase the indigenous Indian attendance. The problem of religious diversity in post *Raj* India seems to have been overcome by introducing a 'Moral Science' subject for non-Christians also, a very constructive idea which the west could do well to copy, instead of abandoning all moral teaching. There were a small number of Roman Catholic, *Irani, Hindu, Sikh , Muslim, Buddhist* and *Parsi* boys at the Church of England (C.of E.) Barnes High School, Deolali up to 1946, whilst I was there. There was always a great deal of rivalry between the C. of E. and Roman Catholic (R.C.) clergy during the founding of the schools, and in sport ever since. Many schools were run exclusively by religious orders, including many convents for the girls and kindergarten, such as the popular Jesus and Mary Convent, Poona and the Good Shepherd Convent, Bangalore, which ran the Sacred Heart Girls School. My elder sister was a boarder at both. My younger sister accompanied my elder sister to the latter in 1937, when only 3 years old.

The R.C. Order of Jesuits was particularly successful with schools. They first appeared in India in 1542, with the Spanish Jesuit Saint Francis Xavier in Goa, where he was finally laid to rest. The Jesuit Father Stevens was the first Englishman to reach India in 1579. Saint Thomas the Apostle in the Christian Bible, whose shrine is in the Madras suburb of Mylapur where he was martyred, is said to have preached Christianity in India shortly after the death of Jesus Christ between 21 and 52 AD. He was followed by Syrian Christians in 315 and 880 AD. Subsequent conversion of Indians to Christianity, apart from *Anglo-Indians* and other mixed races, and mostly Indians of the lower *Shudra* castes, like the *Harijan (Dalits)*, or *Untouchables*, has only amounted to a relatively small percentage of the native *Hindu* and *Muslim* peoples, who represent the bulk of the Indian sub-continent. There were claimed to be 6 million Christians in India at the time of Indian Independence in 1947, or about one percent of the total population. Of these about half were probably *'Malabar'* or *'St. Thomas Christians'* from south India, said to number 5 million in 1971.[11,18,22]

Many schools designed specifically to serve the *Domiciled European* and *Anglo-Indian* children were generally established by their own associations, various trusts and institutions, such as the *Bombay Education Society*, but with only a limited amount of government assistance being available. Many schools had a charity status, and fees were small and dependent upon parents' ability to pay. The fees at La Martinière College,

Lucknow in 1863 varied from a mere Rs15 to Rs 25 each month, for parent salaries of between Rs 150 and Rs 250 each a month, at a time when most school leavers went into the Railways.[21] Other schools demanded and survived on much higher fees, some ultimately were said to exceed those back *Home*, although this is questionable. About 250 boarding schools were still in existence in the 1960s.[14] About 362 designated *Anglo-Indian* schools existed in 1934, with 55,000 pupils. Only 69 schools were located up in the cool climate of the hill country, whereas the remaining 247 schools were in the plains, where the heat of the summer was most uncomfortable, and took its toll of children, especially in the early years of the British *Raj*. Of these schools 153, or 40 percent, with about 34,000 pupils, were controlled by R.C. religious orders; 79 with about 12,000 pupils, were C.of E. Of the remainder 44 with about 5,000 pupils, were of other, or non-denominational; 76 with about 5,000 pupils were Railway schools; 10 with about 1,500 pupils were Government owned. About 80 percent of the pupils were *Anglo-Indian*.[2]

The boarding schools had either a single 9 month term each year, or a 3 and a 6 month term each year, and taught children to *School Leaving Certificate* level, usually based on examinations prepared and adjudicated by the English University of Cambridge. A *Junior Cambridge Certificate* examination was usually held at the age of 13 or 14, and a *Senior Cambridge (School Leaving) Certificate* at 16 to 18 years of age. I am proud to have come first in school for both these examinations in 1944 and 1946 in Barnes High School, Deolali. Local English speaking British Army Schools, or Regimental Schools as some called them, were available, as were Railway Schools, as day schools in cantonments and railway colonies during the *Raj*, for both Military and Railway children, and also other civilian *European* and *Anglo-Indian* kindergarten children. My brother, elder sister and I attended the Royal Artillery Army School at Kirkee, near Poona between 1932 and 1936.

Numerous Teachers' Training Colleges for men and women teachers were also created ultimately in the 20th century by the *Domiciled European* and *Anglo-Indian Communities*, such as Chelmsford College, Murree (1924), (originally at Lawrence School, Sanwar), St Xavier's College, Calcutta and St Mary's College, Poona, so as to accommodate the needs of schools. The Government had opened universities in Bombay, Calcutta, and Madras between 1850 and 1856 and elsewhere later, which taught to degree level acceptable in the west. Many *Domiciled Europeans* and *Anglo-Indians* returned subsequently to Britain and elsewhere in the Commonwealth and the USA, to successfully pursue their careers with distinction.[7] Thomason Engineering College in Roorkee is another internationally well respected technical institution started at this time by Sir Proby Cautley. It was named after the then Lieutenant Governor of the Punjab James Thomason.

When India was granted her independence from the British *Raj* in 1947, and with the consequential exodus of many *European* and *Anglo-Indian* pupils back to Britain, or elsewhere, the *Bombay Education Society* were forced to consider closing Barnes School, Deolali. The decision was successfully reversed by the efforts of the barrister Mr Frank Anthony, the leader of the *Anglo-Indian* community in India, who was responsible for advising the Indian government on the framing of the Indian Constitution. The new Indian Constitution enacted in January 1950 guaranteed the protection of *Anglo-Indian* schools, which were grant-aided on condition that at least 40 percent of pupils were non-*Anglo-Indian*. Despite this in 1953 it is said the Indian Government attempted to make *Anglo-Indian* schools unviable, by restricting entry to *Anglo-Indians* only. In 1954 they tried to change the language of teaching from English to *Hindi*. Both actions were overturned in the Supreme Court. Barnes School, Deolali, with the considerable courage of it's Principal, W.R. Coles, and the efforts of Frank Anthony, had created a precedent for all the other *Anglo-Indian* schools in India by their success.[3,12]

Since 1960 the guarantee of financial assistance to *Anglo-Indian* schools by central government has ceased, though many State governments still provide grants to private schools, including *Anglo-Indian* schools. However under the progressive leader of the *Anglo-Indian Community* Frank Anthony, successful attempts were made to start about 20 new independently financed *Anglo-Indian* Schools all over the country, called the Frank Anthony Schools, where the especial needs of education, culture and English language of the *Anglo-Indian Community* can be preserved, under the control of the *All-India Anglo-Indian Education Institution*. Statistics in 1982 show that there were 220 *Anglo-Indian* schools in existence, of whose teachers only about 18 percent are *Anglo-Indian*, although the position is generally reversed in the Frank Anthony schools.[1,2]

Evelyn Abel, in her well researched book *'The Anglo-Indian Community: Survival in India'* [1] details the development of *Anglo-Indian* education in India since Independence. The *'Council for the Indian School Certificate Examinations'* (C.I.S.C.E.) came into being in 1958, with the able assistance of A.E.T,Barrow, an *Anglo-Indian* former master of Barnes High School, Deolali, during my time there, when the old *Cambridge School Certificate* examination of the *Raj* was replaced by the *Indian Certificate of Secondary Education* (ICSE) examination. Barrow became the the first General Secretary of the Council with Frank Anthony as the first Chairman. Both were the two *Anglo-Indian* representatives allowed on the *Lok Sabha*, the Indian Parliament. *'The Council is an all-India body including in its organisation representatives of the Inter-University Board. The Public Schools (including the military academies or Sainik Schools), Air Force Schools and a large number from the other non-Anglo-Indian English-medium schools all over India are affiliated to the Council.'* [1] The Council School List of 1993 [8] shows that most of the British *Raj Anglo-Indian* Schools are still in use in present day India, Pakistan and Bangladesh, each annotated as *Association of Heads of Anglo-Indian* Schools, with a few post-*Raj Anglo-Indian* schools also. Other English-medium non-*Anglo-Indian* schools are also on the same list, but not annotated. It was noticeable that some schools known to be *Anglo-Indian* during the *Raj*, were not marked as belonging to the *Association of Heads of Anglo-Indian Schools*!

ANGLO-INDIAN PUBLIC & PRIVATE PREPARATORY &/or SECONDARY BOARDING &/or DAY SCHOOLS OF INDIA DURING THE BRITISH RAJ (including school name changes, amalgamations, redundant schools, and some Training Colleges, and a few post-*Raj* schools mentioned in the text.*) With acknowledgements to Hazel Innes Craig,[7] Withbert Payne at internet web-site *www.anglo-indians.com*, Cathy Day at *www.ozemail.com.au/~clday* and the C.I.S.C.E.[8]:

1. Albany Hall Public School, Calcutta
2. All Saints Academy,Tehri
3. All Saints High School, Hyderabad
4. All Saints Diocesan College, Naini Tal
6. Alphonsa Residential School, Kottayam
7. Anglo-Indian Home & Taylor High School for Girls, Poona
8. Archer's School, Calcutta (1789)
9. Ardwise's Academy, Calcutta (early 19th century)
10. Army Schools (numerous cantonment military sponsored day schools)
11. Assembly of God School, Asansol
12. Assembly of God School, Calcutta
13. Auckland House School, Simla (1875), (formerly Punjab Girls School (1866)
14. Auxilium Convent School, Bandel
15. Auxilium Convent School, Calcutta
16. Baldwins Boys School, Bangalore (1880)
17. Baldwins Girls School, Bangalore
18. Bangalore Grammar School, Bangalore
19. Barnes High School,Deolali(*Bombay Education Society* (BES) (1925),(originally Rev Cobbe EIC School, Bombay (1718) & later Christ Church School (BES), Bombay (1825))
20. Benchity High School, Durgapur
21. Bethany College, Darjeeling
22. Bishop Corrie Girls High School, Madras
23. Bishop Corrie Boys Grammar School, Madras (formerly Madras Grammar School 1834, and earlier Madras Parental Academy)
24. Bishop Cotton Boys School, Bangalore (1865)
25. Bishop Cotton Girls School, Bangalore (1865)
26. Bishop Cotton School, Darjeeling
27. Bishop Cotton School, Madras
28. Bishop Cotton Boys School, Nagpur (1863)
29. Bishop Cotton's School,Simla (1867),(Bishops School1866: Simla Public School 1863)
30. Bishop Fisher's School for Boys, Darjeeling
31. Bishop Johnson School & College, Allahabad
32. Bishop Moore School, Marelikara
33. Bishop Westcott's Boys School, Namkum, Ranchi
34. Bishop Westcott Girls School, Namkum, Ranchi
35. Bishop's College, Calcutta
36. Bishop's High School for Boys, Poona (1864)
37. Bishop's School, Seetabuldee

38. Bombay Free School, Bombay (1718) (later Christchurch (1825)
    & Barnes High School, Deolali (1925))
39. Bombay Scottish School, Bombay
40. Boys High School & College, Allahabad
41. Breeks Memorial School, Ootacamund
42. Brigg's School, Ootacamund
43. Cainville House School, Mussoorie (1864)
44. Calcutta Academy, Calcutta
45. Calcutta Free Schools for Boys and Girls (1731) (later
    St. Thomas' Schools)
46. Calcutta Grammar School (1823) (formerly Doveton College, and
    later Calcutta High School, and subsequently St Paul's
    School, Darjeeling1866)
47. Calcutta High School (1830), (formerly Calcutta Grammar
    School (1823), and later St Paul's School, Calcutta and
    eventually Darjeeling)
48. Calcutta Girl's High School, Calcutta
49. Calcutta Marine School, Calcutta (c1924)
50. Cambria Hall, Dehra Dun
51. Cambridge School, Bangalore
52. Campion School, Bombay
53. Campion School, Trichinopoly
54. Capucin Boys School, Madras
55. Carman School, Dehra Dun
56. Carmel Convent High School, Durgapur
57. Carmel School, Bagalpur
58. Cathedral Grammar School, Bombay (1868), (Amalgamated with
    Cathedral Choir School (1878) in 1922 to become Cathedral
    Boys and Girls Schools: now known as Cathedral & John
    Connor Boys & Girls Schools)
59. Cathedral Boys School, Bombay (1922) (now Cathedral & John
    Connor Boys School)
60. Cathedral Girls School, Bombay (1922). (now Cathedral & John
    Connor Girls School)
61. Cathedral Choir School of St. Thomas' Cathedral,
    Bombay(1878), (amalgamated with Cathedral Grammar School
    in 1922 to become Cathedral Boys & Girls Schools, and now
    known as Cathedral & John Connon Boys & Girls Schools)
62. Cathedral High School, Bangalore
63. Cathedral High School, Lahore
64. Cathedral & John Connon School, Bombay (see above)
65. Chudder Ghaut Protestant School, Hyderabad (Deccan)
66. Chelmsford Teachers Training College, Ghora Gali, Murree(1924)
67. Christ Church School, (Bombay Education Society (BES)),
    Byculla, Bombay (1825), (originally Rev Cobbe EIC School,
    Bombay (1718))
68. Christ Church Boys High School, Jubbulpore (1870)
69. Christ Church Girls High School, Jubbulpore (1870)
70. Christ Church College, Lucknow
71. Christ Church School, Madras

72. Christ Church Girls School, Simla
73. Christ the King College, Jhansi
74. Church Park Convent, Madras
75. City Montessori School, Lucknow
76. Clarence School, Bangalore
77. Cobbe (Rev Richard) East India Company School, Bombay (1718) (later became Christ Church School(BES), Byculla (1825) and also Barnes High School (BES), Deolali (1925): now known as Barnes School)
78. Col. Brown Cambridge School, Dehra Dun
79. Constancia School, Dehra Dun
80. Convent of Jesus & Mary, Agra
81. Convent of Jesus & Mary, Ambala
82. Convent of Good Shepherd, Bangalore
83. Convent of Jesus & Mary, Dehra Dun
84. Convent of Jesus & Mary , Lahore
85. Convent of Jesus & Mary, Murree
86. Convent of Jesus & Mary, Mussoorie (1845)
87. Convent of Jesus & Mary, New Delhi
88. Convent of Jesus & Mary, Poona
89. Convent of Jesus & Mary, Simla
90. Convent of Sacred Heart, Bangalore (see also Sacred Heart High School)
91. Convent of Sacred Heart, New Delhi
92. Convent of Our Lady of Providence, Calcutta (1934)
93. Count Montessori Inter College, Lucknow
94. D.B.M.S. English School, Jamshedpur
95. Diocesan Boys and Girls School, Naini-Tal (1869)
96. Don Boscoe School, Bandel (1929)
97. Don Boscoe School, Calcutta (1934)
98. Don Boscoe School, Howrah
99. Don Boscoe School, Liluah (1937)
100. Don Boscoe School, Madras
101. Don Boscoe School, Poona
102. Don Boscoe School, Siliguri
103. Doveton College, Calcutta (1835) (started as Parental Academy (1823), later changed first to Calcutta Grammar School and subsequently transferred to Darjeeling as St Paul's School)
104. Doveton Technical Training College, Madras (1855) (later Doveton High School)
105. Doveton Corrie Girls High School, Madras
106. Dow Hill Boys School, Kurseong
107. Dow Hill Girls School, Kurseong
108. Dow Hill Technical Training College, Kurseong
109. Dr. Graham's Homes, Kalimpong (1947). (formerly St. Andrew's Colonial Homes founded in 1900)
110. Drummond's Dhurumtolla Academy, Calcutta (1813)
111. Durell's School, Calcutta (early 19th Century)
112. Elphinstone High School, Bombay (1856)
113. Ema Thompson School, Lucknow

114. Entally Convent, Calcutta
115. European Girls High School, Allahabad
116. European Station School, Rawalpindi
117. Farrell's Seminary, Calcutta (early 19th century)
118. Female School of Industry for Daughters of Europeans, Calcutta (1832)
119. Female School of Industry for Daughters of Europeans, Madras (1832)
120. Frank Anthony School, Bangalore (1967)*
121. Frank Anthony Public School, Calcutta (1965)*
122. Frank Anthony School, New Delhi (1956)*
123. Garden School, Srinigar, Kashmir (1935)
124. Glenhill Public School, Kurseong
125. Goethal's Memorial School, Kurseong
126. Good Shepherd Convent, Jhansi
127. Good Shepherd School, Madras
128. Good Shepherd Public School, Ootacamund
129. Hallett War School, Naini Tal (1942) (formerly Philander-Smith College, Mussoorie)
130. Hampton Court School, Mussoorie
131. Hebron School, Conoor (1899)
132. Hebron School, Ootacamund, (formerly at Conoor)
133. Higher Military Orphanage, Alipore, Calcutta
134. Holman Institute, Agra
135. Holy Angels Convent, Madras
136. Holy Child Institute, Durgapur (1938)
137. Holy Child School, Calcutta
138. Holy Child School, Ghaziabad
139. Holy Cross High School, Bullia
140. Holy Cross Matriculation School, Salem
141. Hutchings High School, Poona
142. Indian Mercantile Marine Training Ship 'Dufferin', Bombay
143. Infant Jesus Anglo-Indian High School, Quilon
144. Ingraham Institute English School, Ghaziabad
145. Isabella Technical College, Lucknow
146. Julien Day School, Darjeeling
147. Karachi Grammar School (1847)
148. Karagpur High School, Karagpur
149. Khishnagur College, Calcutta (early 19th Century)
150. Kimmins High School, Panchgani
151. Kodaikanal International School (formerly Highclerc School)
152. La Martinière College, Calcutta (1836)
153. La Martinière Girl's College, Calcutta
154. La Martinière College, Lucknow (1840)
155. La Martinière Girl's College, Lucknow
156. Lavinia House, Calcutta
157. Lawrence Military School, Ghora Gali, Murree (1860) (Now Ghora Gali College, Murree)
158. Lawrence Memorial Royal Military School, Lovedale, Ootacamund (1858)

159. Lawrence Military School, Mt.Abu, Rajputana
160. Lawrence (Teachers Training) School, Sanawar (moved to
     Chelmsford School, Murree in 1924)
161. Lawrence Royal Military School,The, Sanawar, Kasauli (1846)
     (formerly Lawrence Asylum & The Lawrence Military School
     after WW1 in 1922)
162. Lewis' Free School, Madras (1698)
163. Loretto Convent, Entally (1843)
164. Loretto Convent, Lucknow
165. Loretto Convent High School, Asansol (1877)
166. Loretto St Mary's Teachers Training College, Calcutta (1912)
167. Loretto Day School, Dharamtalla, Calcutta (1879)
168. Loretto Day School, Sealdah, Calcutta (1854)
169. Loretto House, Calcutta (1842)
170. Loretto Convent, Darjeeling
171. Loretto Convent, Ranchi
172. Loretto Convent, Shillong
173. Loretto Convent, Simla
174. Loretto Convent, Vizagapatam
175. Lower Military Orphanage, Alipore, Calcutta (1783)-(moved in
     1855 to Lawrence School, Sanawar)
176. Loyela High School, Calcutta
177. Loyela College, Madras
178. Madras Grammar School (1834), (formerly the Madras Parental
     Academy, and later Bishop Corrie Grammar School)
179. Madras Female Asylum Orphanage (1787)
180. Madras Male Orphanage (1787), (formerly St Mary's Church
     Charity School (1715), and earlier Pringle's School (1673))
181. Madras Parental Academy
182. Mar Thoma Residential School, Tiruvalla
183. Marian Education Centre, Calcutta
184. Marovkas English Medium School, Margoa
185. Mary Immaculate School, Berhampore
186. Mayo School, Simla
187. Modern Public School, Lalitpur
188. Modern School, Lucknow
189. Montfort School, Delhi
190. Montfort Boys High School, Yercaud, Salem
191. Mount Carmel Convent Anglo-Indian Girl's School, Quilon
192. Mount Carmel School, Hoshioapur
193. Mount Hermon School, Darjeeling (1930) (formerly Queen's Hill
     School for Girls 1895)
194. Mount Zion Residential School, Pathanamthitta
195. Mussoorie International School, Mussoorie
196. Mussoorie School (Maddock's) (1835)
197. Nazareth Academy, Gaya
198. Nazareth Convent, Ootacamund
199. New School, Calcutta
200. New School, Darjeeling, (formerly New School, Calcutta)
201. New English School, Poona

202. Noble School, Hyderabad (Deccan)
203. Oak Grove School (EIR Railways), Jharipari,Mussoorie
204. Parental Academy , Calcutta (1823) (renamed Doveton College (1835)
205. Patna College, (early 19th Century)
206. Petersfield School, Naini Tal
207. Philander-Smith School, Mussoorie
208. Philander-Smith College, Naini Tal, (later became Hallet War School, Naini Tal)
209. Pine Mount Government Girls High School, Shillong
210. Pratt Memorial School, Calcutta
211. Presentation Convent, Kodaikanal
212. Presentation Convent, Quetta
213. Pringle's (Rev) East India Company School, Fort St George, Madras (1673), (later St Mary's Church Charity School (1715)
214. Presidency School, Bangalore
215. Presidency College, Calcutta
216. Punjab Girls School, Simla (1866) (later Auckland School)
217. Queen's Hill School for Girls, Darjeeling (1895)
218. Queen Mary College, Lahore
219. Railway Schools (Numerous day schools at major Railway centres and colonies)
220. Rosary Convent, Hyderabad
221. Sacred Heart College, Bangalore
222. Sacred Heart Girls High School, Bangalore
223. Sacred Heart Boys School, Bombay
224. Sacred Heart Convent, Bhusaval
225. Sacred Heart Convent, Dalhousie
226. Sacred Heart Convent, Howrah
227. Sacred Heart Convent School, Jamshedpur
228. Sacred Heart School, Karagpur
229. Sacred Heart Convent, New Delhi
230. Sacred Heart School, Santa Cruz
231. Sacred Heart Convent School, Simla
232. Sacred Heart School, Yercaud
233. Scindia School, Gwalior (1897)
234. Scottish Church College, Calcutta
235. Scottish Orphanage, Karachi
236. Serampore College, Calcutta
237. Seventh Day Adventists School, Bangalore
238. Seventh Day Adventists School, Calcutta
239. Seventh Day Adventists High School, Dukki
240. Seventh Day Adventists School, Tarlandhar
241. Sheikh Bagh & Garden Schools, Srinigar, Kashmir (1940)
242. Sherwood Academy, Lucknow
243. Sherwood College, Naini Tal
244. Shri Shivaji Preparatory Military School, Bhamburda, Poona
245. Simla Public School, Jutogh (1863) (later Bishop's School)
246. Singamari School, Darjeeling
247. Soon School, Chandh Bagh, Dehra Dunn (1935)

248. Sophia High School, Bangalore
249. Sophia College, Bombay
250. St. Agnes Convent School, Howrah (Calcutta)
251. St. Agnes Convent, Lucknow
252. St. Agnes School, Karagpur
253. St. Aloysius Orphanage, Howrah (1910)
254. St. Aloysius School, Bhusaval
255. St. Aloysius School, Jubbulpore
256.. St. Aloysius School, Madras
257. St. Aloysius School, Vizagapatam
258. St. Andrew's Colonial Homes, Kalimpong (1900) (later
     Dr.Graham's Homes)
259. St. Andrew's School, Darjeeling
260. St. Anne's School, Mazagaon, Bombay
261. St. Ann's School, Chirala
262. St. Ann's Convent, Secunderabad
263. St. Anselm's School, Ajmer
264. St. Anthony's High School, Agra
265. St. Anthony's High School, Allahabad
266. St. Anthony's School, Bangalore (kindergarten for St.Josephs)
267. St. Anthony's High School, Calcutta (1864)
268. St. Anthony's Convent, Jhansi
269. St. Anthony's High School, Lahore
270. St. Augustine's School, Calcutta
271. St. Bede's Anglo-Indian School, Santhone, Madras
272. St. Bede's School, Mylapur
273. St. Bede's College, Simla
274. St. Columbian's School, Madras
275. St. Columbian's School, New Delhi
276. St. Conrad's Inter College, Agra
277. St. Deny's School, Murree
278. St. Edmund's, Shillong
279. St. Edmund's School, Simla
280. St. Edward's High School, Simla
281. St. Fidelis School, Mussoorie
282. St. Francis Xavier Girls High School, Bangalore
283. St. Francis Convent, Coimbatore
284. St. Francis School, Dacca
285. St. Francis Convent High School, Jhansi
286. St, Francis High School, Lucknow
287. St. Francis Anglo-Indian School, Madras
288. St Francis School, Murree
289. St. Francis de Sales School, Nagpur
290. St. George's College, Bombazar, Calcutta (1830)
291. St. George's College, Dehra Dun
292. St. George's College, Mussoorie
293. St. George's Boys School, Hyderabad (Deccan)
294. St. George's Girls School, Hyderabad (Deccan)
295. St. George's School, Ketti
296. St. George's School, Madras (formerly Civil Orphan Asylum)

297. St. George's Boys School (Manor School), Mussoorie
298. St. Germains High Schpool, Bangalore
299. St. Helen's Secondary School, Kurseong
300. St. Helena's School, Poona
301. St. Hilda's School, Ootacamund
302. St. James College, Calcutta
303. St. James School for Boys, Calcutta (1823)
304. St. James School for Girls, Calcutta (1830)
305. St. John's College, Agra
306. St. John's High School, Bandel
307. St. John's School, Bangalore
308. St. John's School, Chandigarh
309. St. John's College, Chowringhee, Calcutta
310. St. John's Vestry School, Trichinopoly (1773)
311. St. John's War School, Kashmir
312. St. Joseph's Academy, Dehra Dun
313   St. Joseph's College, Allahabad
314. St. Joseph's College, Bangalore (1858) (or St Joseph's European
         High School; now known as St Joseph's Boys High School)
315. St. Joseph's College, Bombazar, Calcutta (1853)
316. St. Joseph's College, Conoor
317. St. Joseph's College, Darjeeling (1888)
318. St. Joseph's College, Naini Tal
319. St. Joseph's College, Trichinopoly
320. St. Joseph's Convent, Chandenagore
321. St. Joseph's Convent, Coconada
322. St. Joseph's Convent, Cuttack
323. St. Joseph's Convent School, Ferozpur
324. St. Joseph's Convent, Hoogly
325. St. Joseph's Convent, Jubbulpore
326. St. Joseph's Convent, Kalimpong
327. St. Joseph's Convent, Kamptee
328. St. Joseph's Convent, Kolar Gold Fields
329. St. Joseph's Convent High School, Karachi (1861)
330. St. Joseph's Convent Girl's School, Karachi
331. St. Joseph's Convent, Murree
332. St. Joseph's Convent, Nagpur
333. St. Joseph's Convent, Panchgani
334. St. Joseph's Convent, Patna
335. St. Joseph's Convent School, Tarlandhan
336. St. Joseph's Convent, Vizagapatam
337. St. Joseph's European High School, Bangalore. (part of St
         Joseph's College)
338. St. Joseph's School, Barramullah, Kashmir
339. St. Joseph's School, Bilaspur
340. St. Joseph's School, Bombay
341. St. Joseph's School, Igatpuri
342. St. Joseph's School, Jalpaiguri
343. St. Joseph's School, Madras
344. St. Joseph's High School, Matigara

345. St. Jude's High School, Virnao
346. St. Jude's School, Dehra Dun
347. St. Jude's School, Dehu Road, Poona
348. St. Kevin's School, Madras
349. St. Lawrence High School, Ballygunge, Calcutta
350. St. Maria Goretti Inter College, Bareilly
351. St. Mark's College, Jhansi
352. St. Mark's School, Bangalore
353. St. Mary's Convent Inter School, Allahabad
354. St.Mary's Convent, Jhansi
355 St. Mary's Convent, Karagpur
356. St. Mary's Residential School, Kollam
357. St. Mary's Convent, Kotagiri
358. St. Mary's School, Madras (1645)
359. St. Mary's Church Charity School, Madras (1715), (formerly
360.   Pringle's School (1673))
361. St. Mary's Convent High School (Ramnee), Naini Tal
362. St. Mary's School, Mazagoan, Bombay
363. St. Mary's High School, Mt Abu
364. St. Mary's Convent School, Multan
365. St. Mary's School, Perambur, Madras
366. St. Mary's High School, Poona
367. St. Mary's Teacher's Training College, Poona
368. St. Mary's Technical Training College, Poona
369. St. Mary's Diocesan School, Darjeeling
370. St. Mary's Orphanage, Calcutta (1848)
371. St. Mary's School, Calcutta
372. St. Michael's School, Darjeeling
373. St. Michael's School, Patna
374. St. Patrick's Convent, Agra
375. St. Patrick's Secondary School, Asansol
376. St. Patrick's School, Chandenagore
377. St. Patrick's School, Madras
378. St. Patrick's School, Secunderabad
379. St. Paul's Academy, Ghaziabad, Delhi
380. St. Paul's School, Calcutta (1846), (formerly Calcutta High
        School 1830)
381. St. Paul's Mission School, Calcutta
382. St. Paul's English School, Calcutta
383. St. Paul's School, Jalapahar, Darjeeling (1864) (formerly St
        Paul's School, Calcutta 1846)
384. St. Peter's College, Agra
385. St. Peter's School, Khandala
386. St. Peter's High School, Mazagon, Bombay
387. St. Peter's Boys High School, Panchgani
388. St. Philomena's Orphanage, Jhansi
389. St. Placid's School, Cittagong
390. St. Scholastics School, Chittagong
391. St. Stephen's School, Ootacamund
392. St. Stephen's College, Delhi

393. St. Teresa's Convent, Bombay
394. St. Teresa's Secondary School, Calcutta (1885)
395. St. Teresa's Girls School, Morelali, Calcutta
396. St. Teresa's Girl's High School, Darjeeling
397. St. Teresa's School, Delhi
398. St. Teresa's Day School, Lucknow
399. St. Thomas' College, Dehra Dun
400. St. Thomas' High School, Ambala
401. St. Thomas' Boys Schools, Calcutta, (Calcutta Free Schools
       (1731))
402. St. Thomas' Girls' School, Calcutta
403. St. Thomas' School, Darjeeling (Takdah)
404. St. Thomas' Church School, Howrah
405. St. Thomas' School, Madras
406. St. Thomas' English Medium School, Meerut
407. St. Thomas' School, Ranchi
408. St. Vincent's High & Technical School, Asansol
409. St. Vincent's School, Balasore
410. St. Vincent's School, Poona
411. St. Xavier's College, Bombay (1867)
412. St. Xavier's College, Calcutta (1860)
413. St. Xavier's College, Dacca
414. St. Xaviers College, Jaipur
415. St. Xavier's School, Ahmedabad
416. St. Xavier's Girl's High School, Bangalore
417. St. Xavier's High School, Bombay (1867)
418. St. Xavier's School, Burdwa
419. St. Xavier's School, Hyderabad, Sind
420. St. Xavier's School, Jaipur
421. St. Xavier's High School, Matheran
421. St. Xavier's School, Ranchi
422. St. Xavier's School, Sahibganj
423. Stanes European High School, Conoor, Coimbatore
424. Stewart School, Bhubaneswar
425. Stewart School, Cuttack
426 Tara Hall, Simla
427. Teacher's Training College, Sanwar
428. Trinity Public School, Hyderabad
429. U.K.C.A. School, Kanpur
430. Upper Military Orphanage, Calcutta (1783)
431. Verulam Academy, Calcutta
432. Victoria Boys School, Kurseong (1897)
433. Victoria Training College, Kurseong
434. Welland Smith Gould Boarding School, Calcutta
435. Vincent Hill School, Mussoorie
436. Waverley Convent, Mussoorie
437. Wellesley Girls' School, Naini Tal
438. Woodstock School, Mussoorie
439. Wynberg Allen School, Mussoorie

APPENDIX 3

RAILWAYS OF BRITISH INDIA

'*Passage to India!*
Lo, soul, seest thou not God's purpose from the first?
The earth to be spann'd, connected by network,
The races, neighbors, to marry and be given in marriage,
The oceans to be cross'd, the distant brought near,
The lands to be welded together.'

(*'Passage to India'* by Walt Whitman 1819 - 1892)

THE IMPORTANT NEED FOR RAILWAYS in India was first promoted by Scotsman Rowland MacDonald Stephenson (not related to the famous railway British Engineers of that name), of the Peninsula and Orient (P.&O.) Steamship Company, who was known as '*the father of Indian Railways*', in the 1840s. Although supported by Sir Frederick Halliday, then acting for the Governor General, the introduction of railways was opposed by the East India Company (E.I.C.), who doubted the skill of Engineers to cross the mighty rivers of India and to overcome the considerable risks from flooding and other natural hazards such as white ants, whose consumption of timber (the only material then used for railway sleepers), was phenomenal. They also feared the railways would not be used by the caste-ridden Indian people. They were to be proved grossly wrong on all these counts in due course, and their false judgment delayed the commencement of the railways for a decade, during which the guaranteed financing of the construction of the railways by contractors using private venture capital was thrashed out.

The Railways were a completely new form of mechanically powered and efficient wheel on rail form of transport system in the 19th century. The concept was invented in Cornwall, in southern England, by the brilliant English Mining Engineer Richard Trevithick, who designed and successfully operated the first steam engine locomotive on rails for the tin mines in 1804. His invention was developed by the renowned English Railway Engineer George Stephenson, who pioneered the first successful public passenger and freight steam locomotive, train and railway line in the world in 1825, between Stockton and Darlington, in northern England. His son Robert Stephenson and other British Engineers then proceeded to spearhead the development of steam locomotives and railways in the remainder of Great Britain and the rest of the world, including India and other countries of the British Empire.

Captain Edward Davidson of the Royal Engineers, a Consulting Engineer to the Government of India, in his valuable book of 1861 '*The Railways of India*' [5] made the first remarkable attempt to describe the incredible efforts of British Consulting Engineers and Contractors and their gigantic achievement of construction of perhaps the greatest railway system in the world. The book by the Royal Engineer Lt.Col.E.W.C. Sandes titled *'The Military Engineer in India'*,[12] which followed in 2 volumes in 1933/35, is a remarkable all embracing Engineering classic which includes in the second volume many projects and personalities engaged on the railways, roads and irrigation. *'Permanent Way Through the Khyber'* [2] the personal experience of the pioneer Railway Engineer Victor Bayley in 1939 and *'The Unsung, A Record of British Services in India.'* [6] by Maud Diver in 1945, give a vivid description of the trials of road, railway and irrigation construction in India. A later railway classic was *J.N.* Westwood's *'Railways of India'* [16] in 1974. Other erudite works followed in the second half of the 20th century, including that of Ian J. Kerr in *'Building the Railways of the Raj 1850 - 1900*[9] in 1995, in which he brings in the Indian contribution, the labour dimension, and contractor quality.

Lord Dalhousie, Governor General of India, who in 1845 engaged the competent and enthusiastic English Railway Engineer F. W. Simms as his Consulting Engineer, entrusted railway construction in India at first to private companies. Railways were constructed to a very high standard, but without extravagance, as quality was being monitored by the Government, whilst Contractors were concerned to limit expenditure to ensure profits. Simms was succeeded as Consulting Engineer to the Government of India in 1850 by the brilliant, though controversial, Irish Colonel J. Pitt Kennedy, formerly of the Royal Engineers, for a year, before he left and later became Consulting Engineer to the Bombay, Baroda and Central Indian Railway (B.B.&C.I.R.). The Consulting Engineers to the Governments of Bombay *(Mumbai)*, Madras and Bengal at the time were Captain Crawford, of the Bombay Engineers, Major Pears, of the Madras Engineers and Major W. Erskine Baker of the Bengal Engineers respectively, the latter, later to become Major-General Erskine Baker and subsequently succeeding Colonel Kennedy in 1851 as Consulting Engineer to the Indian Central Government.[5]

The Governor of Bombay Lord Elphinstone, aided and abetted by his Private Secretary Sir Bartle Frere, took a very active interest in the railways in the Bombay Presidency. There, what was to become the first mainline railway in India, the Great Indian Peninsula Railway (G.I.P.R.), commenced operation in 1853, partly to provide a means for exporting cotton to England, as an alternative to the American source, where a drought had destroyed one crop and subsequent crops by the American Civil War. Bombay *(Mumbai)* was to become a major cotton milling and exporting town.

The railway commenced with a 20 mile stretch to Thana, part of the first 35 mile experimental route from the now famous Bombay neo-Gothic Victoria Terminus (V.T.), later designed and built in 1870 by British P.W.D. Engineer Frederick William Stevens, and now called Chatrapati Shivaji Railway Terminus. Kalyan Junction was reached in 1854, at the foot of the Western *Ghats* (mountains). There the railway bifurcated between the trunk route north-east towards Calcutta *(Kolkatta)* and Delhi, and south-east towards Madras *(Chennai)*. Design and construction was supervised by the English Chief Engineer of G.I.P.R. James J. Berkley, with the famous

Figure 12:
BRITISH RAJ INDIA MAIN LINE RAILWAYS
(Showing date of construction)
Legend: GIPR   = Great Indian Peninsula Railway
        BB&CIR = Bombay, Baroda & Central Indian Railway
        EIR   = East Indian Railway
        MSMR   = Madras & Southern Maratha Railway
        NWR   = North Western Railway
        BNR   = Bengal, Nagpur Railway

English Railway Engineer Robert Stephenson, son of the first Railway Engineer George Stephenson, an early President of the British *Institution of Civil Engineers* and Member of Parliament, as Consultant. The crossings of the Western *Ghats*, which rise to peaks some 4,500 feet above sea level, with intermediate ridges 2,500 feet high, were spectacular, with lines passing up and through the *Thul Ghat* to Bhusaval Junction, via Deolali (*Devlali*) (the site of the British Army transit camp in World War 2), and the *Bhore Ghat* to Poona (*Pune*) and Kirkee (*Khadki*) on the *Deccan* plateau (the site of Southern Command of the British Army during World War1 & 2). Although the bulk of the 81 mile stretch from Kalyan to Deolali was completed by 1861, the whole line to Jubblepore (Jabalpur) via Bhusaval was not open until 1870, being delayed by work at *Thul Ghat*. The East India Railway (E.I.R.) had reached there from Allahabad in 1870. The 87 mile line from Kalyan, past Lonavla, Kirkee to Poona, the 42 mile section of which from Khandala was opened in 1858, was even more difficult to construct because of the precipitous *Bhore Ghat*. Although Sholapur was reached in 1860 and the G.I.P. railway connected with the Madras Railway (M.R.) at Rhaichur 450 miles from Bombay, the link with Madras 300 miles further was not opened until 1871. By then there was a continuous mainline rail link, aggregating nearly 5,000 miles, across the greater part of the sub-continent of India, with branch lines already proliferating, (see Fig. 12).

At the time of India's independence from British rule in 1947 there were about 40,500 route miles of railway, which was and still is the largest railway system in Asia, and the second largest system in the world. By 1992 the railway system had reduced to 37,850 miles of track, with over 7,000 stations, and over 11,000 locomotives, including 5,000 steam engines. In 1895 the first steam engine to be manufactured in India, was built in Ajmer, 200 miles south west of Delhi, after many years assembling locomotive parts fabricated in England and shipped out to India. Carriages and other railway train and track equipment began also to be manufactured in local Indian workshops.[5,9,16] My paternal great grandfather was a Foreman Boilersmith at the G.I.P.R. workshop at Byculla, a suburb of Bombay, from 1891 until his early death in 1893.

Meanwhile Colonel Kennedy was building the competing B.B.&C.I. rail link from Bombay to Delhi, supposedly to save cost by using land permitting a flatter ruling gradient. He reached Ahmedabad via Surat by 1870, but did not reach Muttra (for Delhi) until 1909. The eventual cost was greater than many other railways, despite his earlier protestations to the contrary, amounting to an average of £20,000 per mile, as against the cheapest at £7,700 per mile on the Great Southern Railway (G.S.R.) in south east India, opened in 1862. The B.B.&C.I.R. route did however reduce the length of the journey from Bombay to Delhi by nearly 100 miles, from the 956 miles by G.I.P.R.[5,16] The famed B.B.&C.I.R. *Frontier Mail* successfully competed against the G.I.P.R. *Punjab Mail* by several hours, over a journey of approximately 24 hours. However G.I.P.R. claimed to run the fastest train in India since the 1930s, when they introduced the *Deccan Queen* on the railway from Bombay to Poona, covering the 119 miles over the *Ghats* in 15 minutes short of 3 hours. This was converted from steam to electric in the 1929. When I visited India in 1995 this train, which still runs, was but a shadow of its former self, both in condition and time keeping. During the 1990s the remainder of the country was converting gradually from steam to electric and diesel electric. The Indian Government finally decided to stop running steam engines commercially in 1996, except for the line to Darjeeling in the foothills of the Himalayan Mountains. In Pakistan this has also happened, although the steam trains from Peshawer to the Khyber Pass at Landi Kotal were revived again for tourists in the early 1990s.

The crossing of the precipitous Western *Ghats*, from Bombay, especially to achieve the restrictive ruling gradients required by the railway, of between 1 in 37 and 1 in 48, was an arduous and dangerous exploit for the G.I.P.R., and required a degree of Engineering skill of the highest order and ingenuity. Even with the use of reversing stations, there was need for 25 tunnels in very hard basalt rock, totalling 12,000 feet and 22 bridges in the *Bhore Ghat* ascent alone. (Later these reversing lines were replaced by direct gradients, with the construction of further tunnels and viaducts). Steel bridges were usually prefabricated in England and shipped out to India for assembly and erection. Of the 35,000 or so average work force, some 30 percent lost their lives through accident or disease, of which typhus, cholera, small pox, malaria, dysentery and hepatitis were endemic and often reached epidemic proportions. The turnover of the initially all *European* expatriate supervisory staff, which included all the Engineers, Surveyors, and Inspectors, and also many Irish '*navvies*' as foremen, was high also, at 5 percent each year. The intense heat of the summer and monsoon rain deluges were also a sore trial, generating much sickness and damage to the railway. The English Contractor Solomon Tredwell took over from the original Contractor, Henry Fowler and his partner William Frederick Flaviell of London, who withdrew in 1859, just before completing the line from Bombay up to Lonavla at the summit of the *Bhore Ghat*. He died within a fortnight of arrival in India and incredibly his wife Alice Tredwell took over construction, aided by English Engineers George H. Clowson and Swanston Adamson. She was probably the earliest female Civil Engineering Contractor, if not the earliest female Railway Contractor of all time.[9,13] G.I.P.R. later also took a mainline through from Bhusaval to Nagpur, to connect with the Bengal & Nagpur Railway (B.N.R.) from Calcutta. Scottish Engineer Thomas Craig Glover was another enduring contractor involved in the construction of the G.I.P.R., and also the B.B.&C.I. and other railways. Others were Duckett and Stead, George Wythes & Co., Joseph Bray, Wythes and Jackson, Hood, Winton and Mills, Lee, Watson and Aiton, and Norris and Weller. Many of these were locally established and initially had little experience of railway contracting. It was not unusual for the Government Engineers to control the construction of the larger complicated structures like bridges. Contrary to popular belief all the railway contractors were not *Europeans* and *Anglo-Indians*. A very successful Indian contractor on the G.I.P. routes was a Parsee from Surat named Jamsetji Dorabji Naegamwalla.[9] My grandfather was a Foreman Engineering Fitter at the G.I.P.R workshops in Bhusaval (where my father was born) from 1892 until his early death of smallpox in 1905 .

The first 25 mile experimental length of the mainline East Indian Railway (E.I.R.), from Howrah, across the River Hoogly from Calcutta, to Hoogly, on the route from Calcutta to Delhi, supervised by the E.I.R. English Chief Engineer Mr. Turnbull was completed in 1854. The enormous steel cantilever Howrah Bridge over the River Hoogly to reach Calcutta, once the largest cantilever bridge in the third world, was not built until 1942. Before the bridge, reliance was placed on ferries and pontoon bridges. The bridge, which had a 1,500 feet main span, was designed and built by leading British Consulting Engineers, later known as Rendal, Palmer & Tritton. Englishman James Meadows Rendal, who founded the firm in 1838, and was President of the British *Institution of Civil Engineers*, the first in the world, was Consulting Civil Engineer to the E.I.R. in 1858. By 1855 the E.I.R. line opened 121 miles to Raniganj, permitting exploitation of the vast coalfields there. The 1,000 mile continuation to Delhi followed, taking a further 9 years until completion in 1864, with responsibilities split between Mr. Turnbull on the eastern half and first Mr. Purser and later Mr. Sibley on the western half as Chief Engineer. Other lines followed. Considerable resources were expended on embanking the railway and providing ample bridge and culvert capacity to overcome extensive flooding which was prevalent in those days, which resulted in constant disruption and damage during construction. Bridges of considerable size were built, necessitating deep foundations of up to forty feet in the alluvial soils of the great River Ganges basin, resulting in some of the longest bridge structures in the world at the time. These enormous bridges were erected by James Palmer, using Warren trusses prefabricated in England of wrought iron, a material first used for the Iron Bridge at Coalbrookdale in England in 1825. (Steel bridges did not come into use until 1879 in U.S.A.) They included the double-decker bridge with 28 No. 150 foot spans across the River Soane, and the similar 3,000 foot bridge across the Jumna River, a pattern of bridge first used by Robert Stephenson across the very much smaller River Tyne at Newcastle in England.

The considerable size and loss of the *European* and Indian work force through disease and sickness were as bad as for the G.I.P.R., although there were fewer accidents, as construction was physically less arduous. The prevalence of tigers in part of the region presented a novel added life hazard, whilst elephants took their toll of telegraph poles, and white ants consumed timber sleepers at an astonishing rate, until they were replaced by cast iron and concrete. The first Locomotive Chief Engineer on the E.I.R. John Hodgson, died of cholera in 1857 and was succeeded by Lingard Stokes. He enterprisingly adapted locomotives to drive paddle wheels on river barges for use during the Indian Mutiny in 1857, to provide improved transport for the British military to overcome the gap in the railway system still under construction. In the early 1860s Calcutta was also served by the East Bengal Railway (E.B.R.), which ran a main line from the elaborate Sealdah Terminus at Calcutta for about 100 miles towards Dacca (*Dhaka*), with the renowned English Civil Engineer Isambard Kingdom Brunel as its Consulting Engineer. Passengers and freight were trans-shipped at a railhead at Kushtia on the River Ganges and taken to Dacca and Assam by river steamer, because of the almost insuperable difficulties of large rivers and flood prone terrain. More lines subsequently followed. Also the Calcutta & South Eastern Railway (C.S.E.R.) completed a 30 mile line to Canning in 1862, where it had been mistakenly hoped to make a new port for Calcutta, less affected by treacherous river currents, tides and shoals. Amongst the Contractors for the E.I.R., E.B.R. and C.S.E.R. were Burn & Co. and Norris & Co. of Calcutta, Hunt, Bray & Elmsley of London, Mr. Daniel, Mr Ryan, Macintosh & Co., Nelson & Co., Ward & Co., Waring Brothers & Hunt, George Wythes & Co, Charles Henfrey and the famous English Railway Contractor Thomas Brassey of Brassey, Paxton, Wythes & Co.[4,5,9,13,16]

The experimental first 67 mile length of the mainline Madras Railway (M.R.), from Veyasarpandi (Madras) to Arcot, on the route towards Bangalore, situated on the Deccan plateau 3,000 feet above sea level, across the Eastern *Ghats*, based on a survey by Captain Collyer of the Madras Engineers, was completed in 1856. The line later bifurcated at Arkonam to head for Bombay some 750 miles away, and reached the G.I.P. Railway at Raichur 300 miles away by 1871.[5,16]

The first 80 miles of the mainline on the Great Southern Railway (G.S.R.) from Negatapatam on the south-east coast to Trichinopoly was completed in 1862, to be followed by an extension to Erode, and followed later by others. It was considered to have been the cheapest railway constructed in India at the time at £7,700 a mile, there not being any works of great difficulty.[5]

Much disruption and damage was done to the railways in northern India by the rebels during the Indian Mutiny of 1857 and many Railway Engineers and Contractors and their families were injured, or even lost their lives. Others such as the Engineer Richard Vicars Boyle at Arrah, between Patna and Allahabad, joined with the British military forces to protect Railway staff, erect defences, or assist with the movement of military stores. Some even took an active part in hostilities to protect the railway and its goods. Of the E.I.R, Calcutta to Delhi railway, only a 44 mile stretch from Allahabad towards Cawnpore made a small but significant contribution to the British military effort at the time of the Mutiny, with lengths also available between Delhi and Agra, and large mileages out of the main terminuses of Calcutta, Madras and Bombay. There was however no continuity, as much of the remainder of the main lines were still under construction.[4,13]

Whereas the holy River Ganges was always a successful all season waterway for passenger and commerce across the north of India, the north/south communications in western India (now Pakistan) were always a problem even before the railways began, as the River Indus waterway, especially where it passes through the hot, dry, practically rainless Sind desert, was hindered by shallow, shifting channels and silt and rapids at Sukkur. It was decided to effect through communications in the first instance by building a main line railway from Karachi, the sea port founded by the victorious Anglo-Irish General and first Governor of Sind, Sir Charles

Napier, for 110 miles up the west bank of the mile-wide River Indus to Kotri, opposite Hyderabad. This was the first length of what was later to become the North West Railway (N.W.R.) after the Sind and Punjab railways were taken over and managed by the Government for strategic reasons. From Kotri a fleet of river steamers would ship commerce up as far as Multan in the Punjab, located about 500 miles upstream on the River Chenab, a tributary of the River Indus. A further railway would then connect with Delhi, via Lahore and Amritsar, a further 550 miles away. The railway to Kotri, which was designed and built by the Chief Engineer John Bruton, was started in 1856 and completed by about 1861, but delays resulted from the false economy of trying to do without embankments because of the small annual rainfall. This proved very costly in the end, as although the annual rainfall is small in the Sind (less than 4 inches a year), it usually arrived in only one or two showers as a deluge, which resulted in hill torrent flooding of the line with much damage. The River Indus also was prone to increase its volume one hundred-fold in summer, from snow melt in the Himalayan Mountains and *monsoon* rainfall in the Punjab, uncontrollably flooding the plains.

The 700 mile railway up the Indus valley to Multan followed, but whilst this was under construction John Bruton was put in charge of a steamship connection on the River Indus plying from Kotri to Multan, a trip which took 34 days against the current and only a week with. The railway from Multan was started off by Sir John Lawrence, in 1859, later to become Viceroy of India and Lord Lawrence of the Punjab, reaching Lahore in 1865. Construction was not difficult due to the flat desert terrain and relatively few bridges. The 303 mile remaining length of the Sind & Punjab Railway (S.&P.R.) that was, between Armritsar and Ghaziabad junction (Delhi) were completed by the English Contractor Thomas Brassey over a 5 year period between 1865 and 1870. Although the line earthworks were of little consequence over the flat countryside, the number and size of the great tributary rivers of the Indus, the Beas, Sutlej, Guugur, Jumna and Markundah and the many irrigation canal crossings in this rich agricultural land of the Punjab posed a formidable challenge. As with the E.I.R. the bridges were some of the longest in the world at the time, and the foundations were required to be carried down a considerable depth (40 feet or more) into the alluvium to ensure stability, and freedom from scour in these colossal mile wide rivers where channels shift annually and flow in summer flood spates can increase ten to hundred-fold, with potentially disastrous consequences.[5]

Although the great Indian railway system was of considerable help in the Afghan War of 1878 - 1880, the Punjab Northern State Railway (P.N.S.R.), as it was then known, had only reached Jhelum, the nearest railhead to the Afghan border, which was still some 200 miles or so away from Peshawer, to which the railway was not laid until 1881. It was not opened through to the rest of the country until the mighty River Indus was spectacularly bridged with a dual road and rail bridge at Attock in 1883, by the very skilled Irish Civil Engineer, Mr (later Sir Francis) O'Callaghan. Thus was provided a continuous rail connection from Calcutta to Peshawer.

Very large bridges were also required across the Indus tributaries, the Ravi, Jhelum and Chenab, with the Sher Shah bridge at nearly two miles long, and with 17 spans 206 feet long, being the longest bridge in the world when constructed. As with the earlier railways, all the bridge steel trusses were fabricated in England and transported out to India for erection. [9,12]

The construction of the 25 mile section (as the crow flies) of the railway from Peshawar to Landi Kotal at the summit of the famed Khyber Pass and the Afghan frontier followed later. The British continued to fear an invasion of India through the pass, particularly by the Russians, or at their instigation. The Khyber Pass had been used for countless centuries by the invaders of India, from the Aryans in 1500 B.C. (from southern Russia), the Greeks under Alexander the Great in 327 BC, the Kushans of Central Asia in the 1st century A.D., to latterly the *Muslim Moghuls* from Persia (Iran) and Afghanistan from 10th century A.D. onwards, with the Mongols under Genghis Khan between times in the 13th century. The pass is about 3,500 feet above sea level in the Hindu Kush mountains. The railway had already reached Jamrud when construction was eventually started on the final length by the Government in 1920 and not completed until five long years later. The English Chief Engineer from the Royal Engineers, who was later to become Colonel Sir Gordon Hearn, was later succeeded by Major E.P. Anderson of the Royal Engineers. They were assisted by four English Engineers, including two from the Railway Department of the Government of India, namely Mr. W.R. Horn and Victor Bayley, later C.I.E. and C.B.E., who completed the railway with a young Sapper Engineer named Hall.

The route was inhabited by hostile and cruel tribesman known as *Pathans*, much respected as fighters by the British Army, who at first were not enthusiastic about, nor forthcoming in providing labour for the railway, which they felt invaded their territory and their independent way of life. However it is alleged that when the ruse was put out that there could be much plunder available with the slow moving trains, they eagerly agreed to help, and even helped with protecting the construction work from opposing tribesmen. A brigade of British troops, the Seaforth Highlanders, was otherwise billeted at Landi Kotal under the command of a Brigadier, to safeguard the border, and incidentally the Engineers and the railway construction. Construction was very difficult and very eventful, with much tortuous tunnelling, in treacherous unstable shale rock formations. Many of the 34 tunnels necessitated brick lining and numerous bridges were required. Frequent delays were caused by sporadic sniping from members of hostile *Pathan* tribes. Direct tribal contract labour was used for most of the unskilled work, including some of the tunnelling, supervised by a Welsh foreman by the name of Peters. A few of the more difficult tunnels were done by specialist contractors brought in from outside. The heat was intense during the summer months, rising to 120 degrees Fahrenheit in the shade, of which there was none, as the whole landscape is bare rock with little grass and no trees. There was little rain, as the *monsoon* hardly reaches the Khyber, but spectacular thunder storms sometimes created raging torrents down the many *nullahs* (watercourses) for a few hours, with consequent damage. In winter the thermometer dropped to below zero.[2]

Although a railway was completed from Lahore down to Karachi on the coast, bridges across the River Sutlej at Ferozpore and the majestic River Indus at Sukkur had not been constructed by 1878, ferries being relied upon. The former, a dual road above railway bridge, consisting of steel lattice girders spanning 27 No. 70 foot deep piers, across the 4000 foot alluvial river channel, and called the Kaiserin-i-Hind (Empress of India), was completed in 1887. The latter equally spectacular steel cantilever bridge at Rohri near Sukkur, known as the Lansdowne bridge (designed by Civil Engineer Sir Alexander Rendal), was not constructed until 1889, during the Viceroyalty of Lord Lansdowne (1888 - 1893), whose name it bears. The physical and logistic problems with both bridges were considerable, with temperatures in over 110 degrees Fahrenheit and river flows of a million cubic feet per second in *monsoon* spate. Much work was done by hand by thousands of native labourers, with the steelwork prefabricated and shipped out from England.

The railway to the Bolan Pass and Quetta from Sukkur, through Jacobabad and across the Pat Desert as far as Sibi, considered to be one of the hottest places in the world, with temperatures of up to 124 degrees Fahrenheit in the shade, was still under construction in 1878, under the supervision of Englishman Lt.Col. J.G. Lindsay of the Royal Engineers, who was Engineer-in-Chief. The Sind-Peshin railway, as it was first known, then climbed from Sibi, at an altitude of 433 feet above sea level, to the summit at 6,537 feet in less than 50 miles, through atrocious rock and shale. In 1883/86 Brigadier-General James Browne, C.I.E. took control as Engineer in Chief (with Mr Molesworth, Government Consultant) ably assisted by Captain Scott and a young and enthusiastic Lieutenant, later to become Major General Sir George Scott Moncrieff, with the Bengal and Bombay Sappers and Miners. He used assorted regiments of Pioneers, by the first rail route to Quetta from Sibi, through the treacherous and barren mountains to the Harnai Pass. It was fraught with danger because of the unfriendly *Pathan* tribes in the area. Troops were actually needed to protect the construction workers and materials during construction. Working conditions were atrocious, with extreme heat in summer and intense cold in the winter, and sickness, including cholera, which at one time resulted in the death of a fifth of the 10,000 work force, with up to a half off work, in need of evacuation from the area. Despite all this, civil engineering had to be of the highest order, with numerous spiral tunnels in treacherous rock and numerous ravine bridges to obtain the ruling gradient of 1 in 45.[9,11,12]

The Civil Engineer Sir Francis O'Callaghan, referred to earlier, was also responsible for the simultaneous construction of a temporary railway from Sibi to Quetta through the Bolan Pass in 1886, at 1 in 25 gradients considered earlier to be too steep for steam traffic. This was a stop-gap routing along the flood prone valley bottom for most of the way, with winch traction at the steep pass gradients to permit urgent movement of military stores before the permanent route was completed, as an imminentRussian incursion was feared. He also extended the line through the Khojak Pass to the Afghan border in 1892. A permanent route through the Bolan Pass was after all constructed as the main line in the 20th century, replacing the

Harnai Pass route which suffered disastrously from flood torrents and was finally abandoned in 1942.[9,11,12] This final line, which was also a magnificent achievement of Civil Engineering, had 20 tunnels and 326 bridges.

From 1869 to 1880 the Government were engaged unsuccessfully in building their own railways. As there was a shortage of funds at the time, the strong resolve of Lord Dalhousie at the introduction of the Railways in India, to prevent a repeat of the gauge war experienced in England, was overturned by the current Viceroy Lord Mayo. In consequence the cheaper 'metre gauge' (3 feet 3.38 inches) railways were authorised in many areas, including the Southern Maratha Railway (S.M.R.), running from Poona to Bangalore and Mysore via Hubli and Guntakal. Up until then all railways were to the broad gauge of 5 feet 6 inches. Subsequently 2 feet 6 inches, and even 2 feet gauges were also used, usually for private princely state railways, such as the Baroda State Railway (B.S.R.), and for costly mountain railways, such as the Darjeeling Himalaya Railway (D.H.R.), which was constructed by Gilander & Arbuthnot & Co. to an altitude of 7,000 feet above sea level in just 51 miles in 1880. The S.M.R. was amalgamated with the Madras Railway (M.R.) in 1907 to become the Madras & Southern Maratha Railway (M.S.M.R.), when it was taken over by the State, though still remained privately managed; as were also the E.I.R. in 1897 and the G.I.P.R. and B.B.&C.I.R. later at the turn of the century.

Up to 460,000 workman were employed in the construction of the Indian railways at the peak in about 1898, mostly using hand tools, wheel barrows and head pans. Large quantities of soil were shifted by *keens*, a primitive way of scrapping up and depositing the earth, by means of pairs of bullocks drawing a metal edged board scoop. Although heavy mechanical excavators were in use constructing railways in America as early as 1842, they were not used even in Britain until the 1890s. So with an unlimited supply of cheap local labour in India it is not surprising that these costly machines were not used until the 20th century. Many thousands of Indians were also gainfully employed in the manufacture and supply of materials for the railways.[9]

By 1903 about 400,000 persons were employed on the operation and maintenance of the then 30,000 miles of the Indian Railways. By 1915 the numbers employed increased to about 600,000, of which only about 8,000 were *European* and 10,000 *Anglo-Indian*. Up until 1870 all responsible jobs were taken by *Europeans* and *Anglo-Indians*, including the posts of mechanics and engine drivers, most of whom were employed locally and were often former British soldiers. In 1870 the Government declared that all posts should be open to Indians also. However although Indians began to be employed as drivers and mechanics, by 1910 only 47 of the 800 or so administrative posts in the Indian State Railways were occupied by Indians. By 1930 *European* and *Anglo-Indian* engine drivers still predominated on the now 41,000 miles of railway, with *European* drivers especially on the crack Mail and Express main line trains, with Indian firemen. Guards on crack trains were also *European*, with *Anglo-Indians* and Indians on the slower passenger and freight trains. Station Masters at large stations and important junctions were *European* or *Anglo-Indian*, with Indians at smaller stations. Workshop foremen were exclusively *European* or *Anglo-Indian*, with the former tending to hold the post of foremen and works managers.[16]

After Indian Independence in 1947 many of the 'metre' gauge lines were converted to broad gauge to improve efficiency and the railways lost their romantic names of origin, under the central Indian Ministry of Railways at New Delhi, to become the Northern Railway (N.R.), South Central Railway (S.C.R.), Eastern Railway (E.R.), Western Railway (W.R.), North Eastern Railway (N.E.R.), Northeast Frontier Railway (N.F.R.), Central Railway (C.R.) and South Eastern Railway (S.E.R.). Pakistan Railways became a separate system, [16] as did Bangladesh Railways in due course.

During the construction of the railways the Consulting Engineers, Contractors and their men lived in temporary camps at strategic points along the way, and conditions were very harsh. On completion at all the important railway junction and workshop towns, permanent Railway Colonies were built well clear of the Indian city, to house the *European*, *Anglo-Indian* and Indian officers who maintained and ran the railways. These were well planned estates, with *pukka* houses and tree lined roads, primary and secondary schools, often a small market and always Railway Institutes for social gatherings.[7] The Indians usually had a separate institute. Water and electricity were laid on, but not sewerage; the night soil system (humourously described as thunderboxes) were used, cleared daily by a *mehtar* (sweeper). Lesser accommodation was also provided within the regions.

APPENDIX 4

IRRIGATION OF BRITISH INDIA
and
MOHENJO-DARO

*'In rivers, the water that you touch is the last of what has
passed and the first of that which comes'*

(Leonardo Da Vinci 1452 - 1519)

1. Irrigation -

IRRIGATION WORKS BEGAN by the British at the beginning of the
19th century, accelerated after the British Crown took total charge of
Government in India in 1858 and continued right up to Indian
Independence from the British *Raj* in 1947. The prime objective was to
improve and assure agricultural output and reduce the risk of famine which
was endemic in this populous country. Works included the construction of
massive irrigation barrages, canal headworks, falls and thousands of miles
of canals all over India, with some canals the size of the larger English
rivers. These works were originally renovations of the extensive early *Moghul*
seasonal flood, or inundation canals built between the 14th and 17th
centuries, which had been neglected and fallen into disuse as the *Moghul*
empire disintegrated. This was soon followed by ambitious regional
perennial schemes which took control of, and made full use of seasonal flow
to provide water in both *rabi* and *kharif* seasons, thence providing year
round crops and employment.

In north India, the West Jumna Canal (old Shah Jehan), in Punjab
province, which was known as the 'bread basket of India', is credited with
being the first major irrigation project mounted by the British between 1817
and 1820, with the East Jumna Canal in 1830, on the opposite side of the
Jumna river. The former was the work of Captains George Rodney Blane and
John Colvin of the Bengal Engineers. Down in Madras Province Major-
General Sir Arthur Cotton formerly of the Bengal (later Royal) Engineers, a
renowned irrigation expert, dammed the River Coleroon near Trichinopoly in
1834 to 1836 and the River Cauvery a few years later. In 1847 to 1852 he
built a barrage and canals in the Godavri River delta, and another similar
scheme followed on the delta of the Krishna River. Both were ultimately
completed in 1890 and 1898 respectively, and provided irrigation for a
much needed 2 to 3 million acres of Cultivable Commanded Area (C.C.A.).
He was also engaged in 1861 on river works, flood control, and irrigation
canals in Orissa province, for irrigation of over 1.5 million acres in the
deltaic regions of the Mahanadi and Brahmani rivers, and a navigational
canal from Cuttack to Calcutta.[14,16]

Colonel Sir Proby T. Cautley, then of the Bengal Artillery, and a great
rival of Sir Arthur Cotton, and who ironically failed to qualify as an

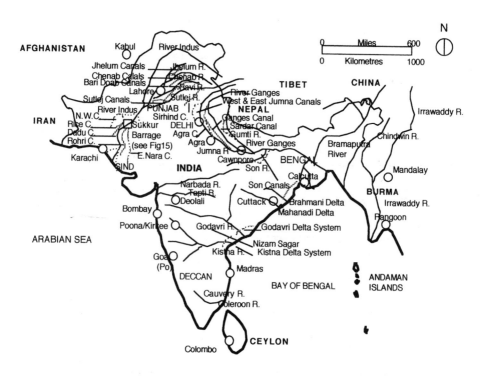

Figure 13:
RIVERS OF INDIA AND BRITISH RAJ IRRIGATION
Legend: ⌒⌒⌒ = Rivers
　　　　 ⌒⌒⌒ = Canals

© *Alfred D.J.(George) Gabb 2000*

Engineer at Addiscombe, was made responsible for the 450 mile colossal Ganges Canal, from Hardwar north of Delhi, to Cawnpore (*Kanpur*). The first phase was from 1842 to 1854, but ultimate completion was not until 1891, after the Lower Ganges Canal had been constructed also (1868 to 1878), with an independent headworks which captured the lower reaches of the original canal well upstream of Cawnpore. Together with the 109 mile Agra Canal (1874), also in the United Provinces, it provided irrigation for a C.C.A. of about 3 million acres of prime agricultural land. The Upper Bari Doab Canal and Sirhind Canals in the Punjab followed in 1851 to 1859 and the Lower Chenab canal in 1892 to 1900, providing assured irrigation for a further 9 million acres of C.C.A. in the 'land of the five rivers.' Another one million acres of C.C.A. were served by the Son Canals in the famine prone Bihar province by 1874.[14,16]

In the Deccan the Mutha left and right bank Canals on either side of the Mutha River through Poona, were completed in 1867, and Kharakwasla Reservoir (Lake Fife) at their head formed when dammed in 1879, to provide a water supply to Poona and district. The great Lloyd dam across the Yelwandi river south of Poona, which formed Bhatghar Lake, and serves the Nira canals, was completed in 1928, having taken 16 years to build. The works submerged a former dam and Lake Whiting constructed in 1885.[17,22] The extensive Deccan irrigation tank (reservoir) systems, which had also fallen into disrepair during the wars and unrest in the 18th and early 19th centuries, were also restored, further reducing the risk of famine which was especially prevalent in western India. Even as late as 1940 large areas of Bombay, Mysore, Central Provinces (C.P.), Rajputana, Bengal and Bihar provinces recorded famines in the previous forty years, with significant areas registering six or more famines.[2]

Maud Diver in '*The Unsung; A Record of British Services in India*'[3] gives a very vivid description of the commendable dedication of most early Irrigation (and road and railway) Engineers, and the extreme discomfort and privation they experienced, during survey and construction, often living for years in tents and *dak* bungalows, enduring the excessive heat and flies of arid desert regions of the Punjab and Sind, or the dense, humid mosquito ridden jungles of south India. In the south-western *ghats* of the *Deccan* a large reservoir was dammed on the westward flowing Periyar River and flow diverted eastward to the parched Madras district of Madura by the indefatigable Colonel John Pennycuick in 1895. Apparently more workman died from sickness and other causes in this one project than there had been fatalities in the Boer War in South Africa.[3]

The cut and thrust of the construction of irrigation works in the early 19th and 20th centuries, the response of the peasant economy and protection from famine achieved, is admirably and comprehensively conveyed by Lt.Col. E.W.C. Sandes in '*The Military Engineer in India*',[14] a classic of British Engineering in India and by Dr. Ian Stone in '*Canal Irrigation in British India.*'[16] The former, in two volumes, covers both Military and Civil Engineering, and also includes roads, railways and the telegraph, with many of the projects and personalities involved.

The early phase of canal construction was carried out by military Engineers of the E.I.C. They became part of the Bengal (later Royal) Engineers, having been first trained at the E.I.C. Military Seminary at Addiscombe, Surrey in England. The best cadets went on for further training in Trigonometrical Surveying, mines and explosives at the School of Military Engineering at Chatham in Kent and the Royal Military Academy, Woolwich in London, also in England. These Engineers formed the nucleus of the Public Works Department (P.W.D.). Later training was provided by the Royal Indian Engineering College, Cooper's Hill, Berkshire, opened in England in 1871. In India, the Thomason Engineering College, Roorkee was opened in the Punjab in 1847. It was named after Lieutenant Governor of the Punjab James Thomason. Later followed the Colleges of Engineering at Poona, Madras, Calcutta (Sibpur), Patna and Benares. By 1932 Roorkee no longer trained military Engineers. This was instead done at the new Indian Military Academy which had opened at Dehra Dun, to train King's commissioned officers in all branches of the Indian Army, including the Engineers.[14] Many of the early Royal Engineers were called back to active military duties during construction, such as during the *Sikh* wars of the mid 1840s and the Indian Mutiny of 1857/58, and most distinguished themselves subsequently in the Irrigation service and elsewhere.

Sir Proby Cautley became Director of Canals in the North West Province in 1848, and member of the Council of India in 1858. Sir Arthur Cotton retired from service in 1862, and became a Consulting Engineer to private canal companies. Among other leading Irrigation Engineers were Major-General William Wilberforce Greathed, who was in the *Sikh* Wars of 1840s, a Consulting Engineer to the East Indian Railways at Allahabad in 1855-57, was wounded at the siege of Delhi, and acted as Directing Engineer at the siege of Lucknow in the Mutiny, was in the China campaigns of 1857-60 and became Chief Engineer of the North West Province Irrigation Department. Colonel Richard Baird-Smith was in both *Sikh* wars of the 1840s, Chief Engineer at the siege of Delhi in the Indian Mutiny, and became Superintendent-General of Irrigation in 1857. Lieutenant-General Henry A. Brownlow was also at the Mutiny, and became Inspector-General of Irrigation in 1882 . Robert Napier became Chief Engineer of the Punjab in 1849, and later Commander-in-Chief in 1870, and Lord Napier of Magdala after the Ethiopian campaign of 1867, which he led. Scotsman Colonel Sir Colin Campbell Scott Moncrieff was also in the Mutiny, and later Chief Engineer of Burma in the late 1870s, became President of the Indian Irrigation Commission in 1901.[14] Also his nephew, later Major General Sir George Scott Moncrieff, was engaged on the Ganges and Swat canals and the Sind-Peshin Railway between various Afghan campaigns in the 1880s.[11] Major General Sir William Erskine Baker was in the *Sikh* wars, and became a member of the Council of India in 1861. Lieutenant-General James Crofton became Inspector-General of Irrigation in 1874. Lieutenant-Colonel Joseph H. Dyas became Chief Engineer of the North West Province in 1864. Scotsman Sir John Benton became Inspector General of Irrigation, Englishmen Colonel Sydney Jacob and his brother Colonel Sir Lionel Jacob who became Secretary to P.W.D. in India. Others were Sir John Ottley, Major Sir Popham Young and Sir Thomas Ward who became Chief Engineer of Irrigation in India.[3] Another was Colonel Henry Yule, who was in the *Sikh* wars, and became a member of the Council of India in 1875. He is best remembered for writing *'Hobson-Jobson, A Glossary of Colloquial Anglo-Indian Words and Phrases, and of Kindred Terms, Etymological, Historical, Geographical and Discursive'* in 1886.

The Marquis of Dalhousie, Governor General of India (1848-1856) first outlined proposals for loan finance for irrigation projects. He had abolished the Military Board which had supplied Engineers for civil projects, substituting instead Chief Engineers in each local government area. He established the basis for the formation of the Public Works Department (P.W.D.) in 1854, but the onset of the Indian Mutiny delayed progress. Lord Lawrence of the Punjab, Viceroy of India (1863 - 1869), increased canal construction. He was greatly concerned about the misery and suffering resulting from the constant droughts and famines in the country, and was through his persistence given *carte blanche* by the British government to execute irrigation works wherever essential on an urgent basis, using loan capital where necessary, to avoid the interminable delay in London. In 1866 the P.W.D. was divided into military, civil and railway branches, the civil branch including irrigation. Colonel Richard Strachey, formerly an Engineer on the Ganges Canal, became the first Inspector-General of Irrigation in India, stationed at Calcutta. He was responsible for forming separate branches of the P.W.D. in each of the Presidencies of the E.I.C. in 1867, which took charge of irrigation, for which 30 Civil Engineers were sent out from London. Principally due to the pressure put on the Government by Sir Arthur Cotton, the construction of irrigation works by private enterprise commenced with the formation of the East India (Orissa) Irrigation and Canal Company in 1861 and the Madras Irrigation Company in 1863. The Government gave a 5% guarantee of £1 million capital and grants of land for the latter only, such as had been adopted for the construction of the railways. The Government was to receive half the profits and retain the right of purchase of all shares after 25 years. The former included the irrigation of the deltaic regions of the Mahanadi and Brahmani rivers on the east coast, river flood control and a navigational canal between Cuttack and Calcutta. The latter was the initial stage of a grandiose scheme devised by Cotton for irrigation and navigational canals across the Deccan. These were on and between the Tungabadra, Krishna and Penner rivers in the east, and included a 50 mile canal from the Krishna to Madras, a 600 mile canal to Poona in the west, and another from Ahmednagar to Mangalore, which latter were never built. Both schemes had far exceeded estimates when bought back by the Government in 1869 and 1882 respectively.[1,16] By 1869

'there was not a province in the whole of India in which extensive surveys for canals had not been made, new canals projected or approved of, and, in many cases, begun, old ones remodelled, embankments against disastrous floods strengthened, and the system of canal management generally reformed.' [1]

In the Sind, in present day Pakistan, archaeological excavations at the ancient ruined city of Mohenjo-Daro, show that irrigation was practised there using the uncontrolled overspill of the River Indus during summer floods as early as in circa 2,500 B.C. (see later). And that other contemporary ancient towns and villages of the prehistoric Indus civilisation were also just as reliant on the river as the present day residents of the Sind. Their location gives a general indication of the ancient courses of this great river, which is one of the longest in the world. Later ancient cities of Aror (or Alor), five miles south east of Rohri, identified by Alexander's conquest in 325 B.C., which some say existed for more than a thousand years as the capital of northern Sind, and later 7th century Brahmanabad, fifty miles north of Hyderabad, gave further evidence of this. During historic times the Indus has migrated across the fifty mile wide flood plain in the Sind, and for long periods had two channels, before settling down to one. The present course of the Nara Canal is alleged to once have been the course of the River Sutlej, with a separate outlet to the sea, before it changed course to join the Indus at Panjnad, with its lower channel becoming the old Hakra river.[10]

In the 16th century the *Moghul* Emperor Akbar, who was born in Umarkot in the Sind, incorporated the Sind into the *Moghul* Empire. The *Moghuls* constructed canals and embankments alongside the River Indus to provide a small degree of flood control, thus limiting sheet flooding. By the 18th century these were in very poor condition and improvements were badly needed. After his conquest of the Sind in 1843, Sir Charles Napier began improving the canals there, and also established a water supply and harbour at Karachi. By the mid-nineteenth century onwards excessive shortages of irrigation water were experienced as a result of the improvement of canals, and the construction of new canal headworks and river barrages in the Punjab. The existing Sind inundation canals were consequently also enlarged and extended and head regulators added at the River Indus, and cross regulators built at intervals along the canals to improve and control water supplies. Watercourses off the canals were controlled by special outlets. Previously erected flood protection riverside bunds were also repaired to better control the devastating floods that swept across the country. In time, and into the 20th century, secondary, or loop, bunds were constructed behind and parallel to the riverside bund, especially at river meanders where the main bunds were susceptible to breaching. I found it awe inspiring in 1964 to watch operations at these loop bunds, when a breach is expected. A cut is excavated in advance through the bund downstream, but within the same loop, and the breaching river flows calmly through the loop and out again to its former channel in complete control![7]

On the west bank of the River Indus north of Sukkur, Sir Bartle Frere, the dynamic Governor of Bombay, initiated remodelling works on the Begari Canal in 1851, which were completed by 1856. The Desert Canal improvement was proposed by Colonel (later General) John Jacob of the Sind Horse, and Commissioner for Sind, revered as a saint in the Sind, and after whom the town of Jacobabad was named, to encourage the former Baluchistan tribes to settle down to agriculture. It was started in 1873 and remodelled in 1900. The Unhar Canal was improved (1884 to 1887). A large

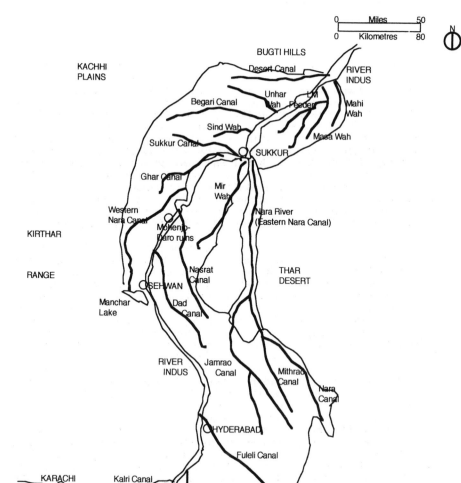

Figure 14:
SIND IRRIGATION - INUNDATION
CANALS 1925
Legend:

〰 = Limit of irrigation
〰 = Main canals

© *Alfred D.F.(George) Gabb 2000*

river bund was constructed alongside the Indus against flooding between Kashmore and Sukkur (1875 to 1887). Below Sukkur on the west bank, the Ghar Canal was improved in 1855, the Sukkur Canal between 1865 and 1870 and the Western Nara Canal from 1892 to 1898. The huge flood protection bund surrounding the irrigated tract, to protect it from the flash floods brought down from the mountainous Kirthar Range, was partially in place by 1920, but not completed from Sukkur to Sehwan until 1935. Below Hyderabad, and near the ancient town of Tatta, the Baghar and Kalri inundation canals were developed from ancient deltaic rivers, abandoned as the delta of the River Indus at the Arabian Sea moved southwards. They are said to have had outfalls to the sea as late as 1817 and 1890 respectively. These were not improved until between 1932 and 1942 [7] (see Fig 14).

On the east bank of the Indus above Sukkur, the Kasimpore to Nabishah flood bund was constructed in 1875 and reconditioned in 1928/29, but river spill still continued. However after construction of the Lundi-Mirpur inundation Feeder Canal in 1940, with its right bank acting as a river bund, only 39 miles remained unprotected between Kashmore and Sukkur. Between Sukkur and Hyderabad, the area nearest the River Indus was first irrigated direct from the river by a large number of inundation canals, the most important of which were the Mir, Nasrat, Dad, Sarfraz and Gul Wahs. The Dad and Nasrat Canal systems were remodelled between 1901 and 1903. Much land however was still reliant on lift irrigation from the canals. Further east towards the vast Thar Desert the area was irrigated by the Eastern Nara inundation canal, which followed the meandering natural channel of the ancient Hakra River for nearly 200 miles from Sukkur, through sand dunes and depressions. It's difficult inlet conditions were improved by a new cut in 1858, and a flood diversion bund at Sukkur in 1917, and its channel was deepened in 1885 and 1894 in most arduous conditions. Of the major canals fed, the Mithrao was constructed in 1879, with a head regulator in 1904, and the Jamrao was completed in 1899. Below Hyderabad the east of the River Indus in the old Indus delta was irrigated by several inundation canals, the major ones of which were the Fuleli, Hassan Ali and the Pinyari. The Fuleli greatly improved in 1857, and this and other canals were remodelled between 1932 and 1942, as it was feared that additional withdrawals in the Punjab, and at the new Sukkur Barrage works (see later), would also deplete supplies in the river. Prior to any barrage construction across the River Indus in the Sind the inundation canals on both banks of the River Indus were irrigating only about 4 million acres [7] (see Fig 14).

Following the continued depletion of flow in the River Indus, by increased extractions in the Punjab, water supply to the inundation canals of the Sind became very uncertain, with disastrous effects on the agricultural output in years when the river was very low. Lt. Colonel Walter Scott, Superintendent of the Canal and Forest Department in 1846, was given credit for the conception of a barrage across the River Indus at Sukkur. Later schemes followed by Lieutenant (later General) J.G. Fife in 1855, and by Dr.T. Summers, Superintending Engineer in 1906 and 1910. The final scheme designed by Mr (later Sir) Arnold A. Musto C.I.E., then an

Executive Engineer, Indian Service of Engineers (I.S.E.), was approved in 1923, following the support of Sir Henry Lawrence, Commissioner for the Sind, and great nephew of Brigadier-General Sir Henry Lawrence of Punjab fame. Sir Thomas Ward C.I.E., M.V.O. and Sir M. Nethersole, Inspectors General of Irrigation also gave it their blessing, and construction commenced in 1925. Construction was by direct labour and was supervised by Mr (later Sir) Charlton S.C. Harrison C.I.E. (I.S.E.), the Chief Engineer. He was aided by Superintending Engineers S.C. Mould, W.N. Cartland, R.B.MacLachlan, D.R. Sawhney, A. Gordon, and D.R. Satarawala, and A.A.Musto,C.I.E., then the project designer, together with 41 Executive Engineers (XEN), including 19 Indians, 4 British Assistant Executive Engineers (AXEN), including 2 Indians from the ISE, and 47 Indians from the Bombay Service of Engineers (BSE). The impressive Lloyd Barrage (better known as the Sukkur Barrage) was nearly a mile long, and was built across the River Indus, below the Sukkur gorge, about 250 miles north north east of Karachi. It was named after Sir George Lloyd, the Governor of Bombay, who administered the Sind province. It has 66 spans each with 60 feet wide 50 ton steel rising gates. Incorporated above the barrage are 7 huge new head regulators controlling the discharge to seven main feeder canals. Construction of the barrage, together with canal regulators, required about 100 thousand cubic yards of concrete, nearly one million cubic yards of superstructure masonry, cut stonework, rubble foundation masonry and stone pitching, together with 80 thousand square yards of steel sheet piling. Concrete mixing and craneage was heavily supplemented, as in present day Pakistan, by hundreds of panniered donkeys and women with head pans. All the stone masons and gangers were men.[8]

The main Sukkur Barrage feeder canals are the North West, Rice, and Dadu Main Canals, all up to 100 miles long on the west bank, and the almost 200 mile long Rohri and Eastern Nara Main Canals, and the less than 50 mile long East and West Khairpur Feeders on the east bank. All but the Eastern Nara and the East Khairpur Feeder were new canals. The old inundation canals were otherwise incorporated in the new canal system wherever possible. The barrage with its 6,000 mile canal system served an area nearly 250 miles long from above Sukkur to the same latitude as Karachi on the Arabian Sea, and about 75 miles at the widest, equivalent to a land mass larger than Wales. The largest main canals are over 100 yards wide, or as large as major rivers in Britain. Forty six steam and diesel mechanical dragline excavators were used, including some of the largest Ruston Bucyrus manufactured machines in the world, and including one named 'Jacob Bahadur', after the revered John Jacob. The machines excavated 54 percent of the total of about 200 million cubic yards of earth. The remainder was shifted by *keens*, a primitive way of scrapping up and depositing the earth, outside the canal bed, by means of pairs of bullocks drawing a metal edged board scoop, a system adopted for earlier canals. The scheme was completed in 1932, only nine years after the scheme inauguration in 1923, at a cost of £15 million then, including £4.3 million for the Barrage and Headworks, and £3.4 million for all machinery, of which latter £800 thousand was for the dragline excavators. It was opened by His Excellency The Earl of Willingdon G.M.S.I., G.C.M.G., G.M.I.E., G.B.E.,

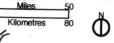

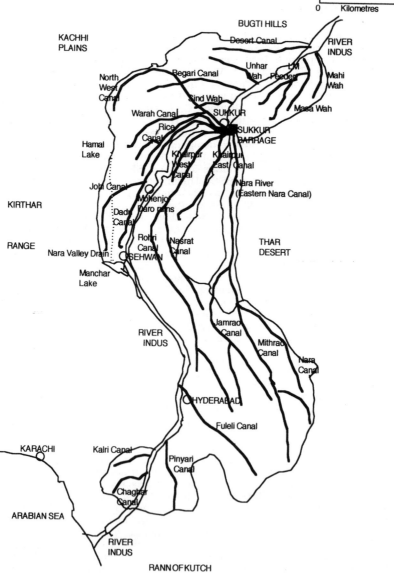

Figure 15:
SIND IRRIGATION - SUKKUR (Lloyd)
BARRAGE & MAIN CANALS 1932 &
REMAINING INUNDATION CANALS
Legend: ■■ = Barrage & main canals

         = Limit of irrigation

         = Main drains

Lloyd's Barrage across the River Indus at Sukkur in 1964

Rohri (Feeder) Canal near Sukkur in 1964

Viceroy and Governor General of India on 13th January 1932. The project was acclaimed an incredible feat of British Civil Engineering, executed in a harsh desert terrain, in a very flat alluvial plain where a land slope of one foot in five thousand was cause for excitement to an Irrigation Engineer. The Gross Commanded Area (G.C.A.) amounted to about 8.08 million acres (12,500 square miles), of which about 7.18 million acres was the Commanded Cultivable Area (C.C.A.), making it the largest irrigation project in the world at the time. Prior to the barrage only about 2.4 million acres had been irrigated in the Sukkur Barrage command area. The result of the barrage scheme was that assured irrigated *rabi* (winter season) crops of wheat, oilseeds, fodder and sugar cane could be grown for the first time. Previously only *kharif* (summer season) crops of rice, *jowari* (sorghum), cotton and fodder were assured irrigation water [7,8,12,13] (see Figs. 13, & 15).

Many other major canal works were also completed in the 20th century all over the country. In the Punjab these included the Jhelum Canal, Upper Chenab Canal and Lower Bari Doab Canal by 1918, the Sutlej Canals by 1938, and the Haveli and Rangpur Canals by 1943, adding 6 million acres of C.C.A. The Sardar Canal in the United Provinces and Nizam Sagar irrigation reservoir in Hyderabad State added a further 2 million acres of C.C.A. by 1931.[2,16] In 1937 Sir William Stampe, Chief Engineer of the U.P. Irrigation Department of the P.W.D. completed the great Ganges Canal Hydro-electric Scheme in 1937. He was awarded the Kaiser-I-Hind medal 1st Class (gold) from King George V in 1927 for '*Pubic Service in India*'.[20] In 1948 the area of land irrigated in India and Pakistan was said to amount to over 60 million acres, which was about a third of the irrigated land world wide.[9] These irrigation projects greatly increased food production against the constant threat of famine in the sub-continent (see Fig. 13).

Despite improvements to the canals in the Sind they continued to suffer from shortages, due to withdrawals in the Punjab. Two new barrages were conceived in 1940 in the inundation canal areas remaining north of Sukkur and below Hyderabad. In 1945 the '*Sind-Punjab Agreement*' was signed by the governments of the Punjab and the Sind respecting the sharing of water in the River Indus and its four Punjab tributaries, to protect the riparian rights of the farmers of the Sind Region downstream. Meanwhile Indian Independence and partition of the country between India and Pakistan intervened on 15th August 1947, in which the sharing of the waters of the five Punjab rivers had to be put on a more clear cut basis, so that each country could operate without fear of duplicity from the other. After years of negotiation between the two new countries agreement was reached and the '*Indus Waters Treaty*' signed in 1960. This gave the full use of the waters of the Ravi, Beas and Sutlej rivers to India, and similar rights to Pakistan for the waters of the Indus, Jhelum and Chenab rivers. The treaty was to come into effect in 1970, allowing Pakistan 10 years to undertake a programme of Link Canals from her remaining rivers to make good the supply for her irrigation formerly fed from the Ravi, Beas and Sutlej. The Triple Project transferred water by link canal from the River Jhelum by the Kashmir border to the Chenab, and a second link took the

Chenab headwaters across the Ravi to the Granji Bar between the lower reaches of the Chenab and the Sutlej. The Thal scheme serves the area between the Jhelum and the lower Chenab and the Indus, with canals offtaking at the new Jinnah Barrage, named after the first Governor General of Pakistan Mohammed Ali Jinnah, across the Indus at Kalabagh, which was built since partition.[2] The Taunsa Barrage was also built lower down the Indus a bit later. The Mangla Dam was built on the Jhelum at the Kashmir border in 1967 and the Tarbela Dam was completed in 1975, on the higher reaches of the River Indus.

Meanwhile the two new barrages across the River Indus in the Sind had been finally designed and ultimately completed by Pakistan, after Indian Independence from the British *Raj* in 1947. These were the Ghulam Mohammed Barrage and Canal System, with a barrage at Kotri, near Hyderabad, nearly 200 miles south of Sukkur and 100 miles north east of Karachi, completed in 1955, and the Gudu Barrage and Canal System, with the barrage located at Kashmore, 80 miles north east of Sukkur, completed in 1961. So for the whole Sind the irrigated areas were raised to a G.C.A. of 14.73 million acres and a C.C.A. of 12.99 million acres.[7,18](see Fig. 16). The Kotri Barrage was named after the Governor-General of Pakistan Ghulam Mohammed. Both barrages and associated canals were designed and constructed 'in-house' by Pakistani Engineers. The United Nations Technical Assistance Board experts assisted during the construction phase of the Gudu Barrage. The Gudu Barrage and Canals system were formally opened by the President of Pakistan, Field Marshal Mohammed Ayub Khan N.Pk., H.J. on 1st March 1963, and were completed at a cost of only about £35 million, of which the barrage cost was about £16 million, without outside financial aid.[19]

However, due primarily to the wastage of irrigation water through its misuse, leakage from canals, the wide spread growth of *pancho* rice and in particular the absence of land drainage, water tables in a large area of the Sukkur Barrage irrigated tract of the Sind had become seriously elevated in the 1950s resulting in waterlogging, and a progressive salinisation of the soil. The knock on effect of this was the reduction of crop yields, and the destruction of soil structure making it impermeable to natural drainage and resulting in the abandoning of many acres of once good agricultural land. During the *Raj* the British had only installed a token amount of land drainage in the barrage command, consisting mainly of the Nara Valley Drain into Manchar Lake, on the west bank of the Indus, between Sukkur and Sehwan. It was however never provided with adequate subsidiary drains into it. As the water table was exceedingly low when the Sukkur Barrage was constructed in 1932, there was little urgency for this, even up to the time that the British left India in 1947. Subsequently, more and more land was irrigated, and after Indian Independence the need for drainage grew and eventually the Water & Power Development Authority (W.A.P.D.A.) of Pakistan called in experts from Britain in 1961 to investigate this.

I was a Resident Engineer with a consortium of two British consultants who spent five years in Pakistan between 1961 and 1966,

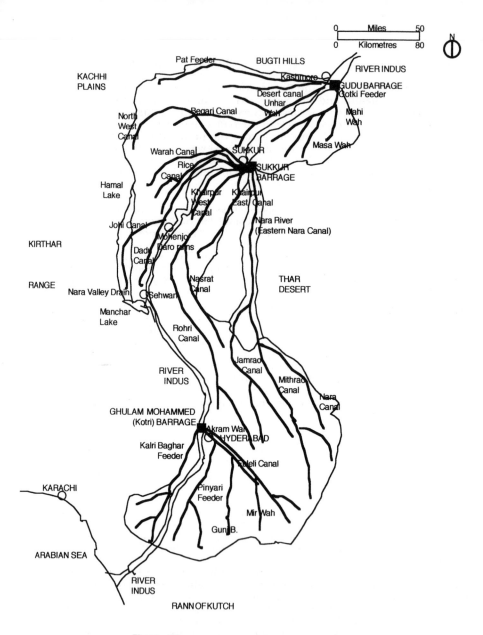

Figure 16:
SIND IRRIGATION - SUKKUR (Lloyd) BARRAGE (1932) & POST BRITISH RAJ GHULAM MOHAMMED (Kotri) BARRAGE (1955), & GUDU BARRAGE (1961) & MAIN CANALS.
Legend: ⌒⌒⌒ = Extent of irrigation

■━━ = Barrages & main canals

© *Alfred D.F.(George) Gabb 2000*

engaged on the *Lower Indus Project* (L.I.P.). They were Sir Murdoch MacDonald & Partners (M.M.P.), Consulting Civil Engineers of London, (now part of Mott MacDonald P.L.C.of Cambridge and Croydon, London, U.K.) and Hunting Technical Services (H.T.S.) of Elstree, Hertfordshire, U.K., Agriculture and Soil Specialists and Surveyors. The expatriate Civil Engineers were spearheaded by G. Richard Hoffman, Chief Engineer, at Lahore, James I.M. Dempster, Regional Engineer with Roy F. Stoner, Deputy Regional Engineer, at Hyderabad, and myself, Alfred D.F. (George) Gabb, Engineer-in-Charge at Sukkur. I later became Project Development Engineer at Hyderabad. I also investigated the serious disintegration from waterlogging and salinity of the ruins of the ancient city of Mohenjo-Daro, (see later). The other expatriate Civil Engineers on L.I.P. investigation were John F. Robson, J. Barry Downs, Gavin Gardner, William Pemberton, Peter Johnson, Patrick Bankart, Louis Renner, David Wardle, Ivan Lorant, Peter Farmer, Anthony Hanson, Roy Sledger, Donald Milne, David Donald, Paul Macdonald, Alan Scott, Peter Drury, Frederick Sharrat, Clive Newey, Keith Curtis, John Bartlett, Alan Bannister and Hugh Williams, with Major John Shebbiere the Administration Officer. The Project Manager in Lahore was Jack H. Burke. In London the Engineer-in-Charge was Alexander A. Middleton (Partner), a former Colonial Irrigation Engineer, Edward Sephton, Gerald Lacey, a former British *Raj* India Irrigation Department Chief Engineer, United Provinces, and a canal specialist and A.M.R.Montagu a former Punjab P.W.D. Irrigation Chief Engineer. At the peak of the investigations there were up to thirty expatriate and four Pakistani Civil Engineers, which latter were Nadir Khan, Masood Khan, H.Jokio and M.Delvi, engaged on the investigation. Engineers Alan Smith, Roger Dembrey, Jeffrey Edmonds and Joseph Knight and Cyril Morris on administration, joined the staff for the Khairpur contract in 1963. The W.A.P.D.A. Chief Engineer was Sayid Hamid. (Note: The distinctions and qualifications of expert Civil Engineers are respectfully omitted for brevity).

Stanislaus Radwanski of H.T.S. led a team of about 40 expatriate agricultural, soil survey and mapping experts, the senior officials of which were James Harbord (Chief Agriculturalist), Bass Van Keulan (Senior Agronomist), Frederick Collier (Senior Soil Scientist), Peter Naylor (Senior Agricultural Economist) and William Trevitt (Cartographer & Chief Draughtsman). Other expatriate experts were Michael Cooper, Arry Kamphorst, Luk Van Douveren, Stanley Weston, Reen Ysselmuidin, Wiktor Bakeiwicz, Ian Carruthers, Patrick Wardle, Michael Gubbins, John Pryde, Michael Grundy, Andrew Seager, Edward Quicke, Joe Murphy, Richard Peters, Michael Palmer, Roger Buckingham, Ian Halse, Derek Holmes, Jack Gill, Norman Goodwin, Gordon Stiven, Arthur Ashworth, Keith Crawford, Elwyn Griffiths, Robert McDorman, Peter de Jaeger, Ian Alsop, R.O'Sullivan, G. Dean, Jan Van der Laan, John Webberley, Keith Valentine and J. Rainmaker. Also in administration was Archibald Forbes and Jock King, who were in turn Regional Managers in Sind, and Stanley Richards, Administration Manager and Derek Layton, Transport Manager. Numerous Pakistani Agricultural and Soil Surveyors, and lower cadre employees supported the team. Vernon C. Robertson and Mr Weatherhead were the Directors in Charge at H.T.S. in England. and Thomas Jewitt was the

Scientific Expert. Dr. Hub Cremers was the amiable and invaluable Dutch Medical General Practitioner (Note: The distinctions and qualifications of the Scientific experts are omitted respectfully for brevity).

The L.I.P. Consultants started with investigations and reports for individual land drainage schemes in the Sukkur Barrage command, but it soon became evident that the irrigation and land drainage systems of all three barrage commands in the Sind needed to be investigated collectively. In consequence W.A.P.D.A commissioned them to prepare comprehensive proposals for irrigation and land drainage, to both master the problem of waterlogging and salinity, and provide for increased agricultural productivity in the whole Sind region. The result of their investigation was the *Lower Indus Report* 1966, [18] recommending perhaps the largest Irrigation and Drainage joint project in the world, covering an area equivalent to the land mass of England. The report recommended a new mile wide, million cusec capacity barrage across the River Indus at Sehwan, the overhaul and remodelling of the whole Sind irrigation system, with the installation of land drainage over the whole area. Apart from the new barrage at Sehwan, and its gigantic 36,000 cusec, 74 mile long feeder canal, the project involves the duplication of distribution canals, and the construction of networks of open drains matching the irrigation canals, with massive outfall drains. Of the new main outfall drains, the Right Bank Outfall Drain is 163 miles long, discharging into the Indus at Sehwan, whilst the Left Bank Outfall is even longer at 257 miles long and discharging into the Arabian Sea. Each of these massive drains are the size of the largest English rivers (see Fig. 17). Extensive areas were to be drained by numerous tubewells and sub-soil tile drainage, the sweeter water from the former being reutilised. It is planned to exploit only the best land, to the exclusion of land suffering from high salinity, although some of this may be reconsidered at a later date. It is expected to increase crop yields/acre by over 3 times for wheat, cotton, and rice, and over 4 times for sugar cane. Development of communications and power supplies in the Sind were proposed, with new and improved trunk and main roads, and much increased power, and improved power distribution. Improved processing, marketing, farm and livestock management, better crop varieties and livestock, use of fertilisers, farm finance, and farm research facilities was also recommended.[18]

The proposed and ongoing L.I.P. irrigation and land drainage works, (now supervised by Mott MacDonald Group) are estimated currently at several billion pounds sterling. Construction of works was programmed originally to take a period of 25 years of continuous construction, but with the constraints of labour, international loans, and local funding, it will probably take twice as long to complete. Khairpur Project, the first construction contract, commenced in 1963. The vast Left Bank Outfall Drain started in 1975 funded by the World Bank, and is all but complete, but not before the outfall had to be extended a further 30 miles nearer Karachi to avoid discharging saline water into the Rann of Kutch, where conflict could arise with India. Other works have included twinning of the canal system, irrigation and drainage tubewells, canal seepage drainage, and subsurface drainage on the left bank of the Indus, in central Sind, in the

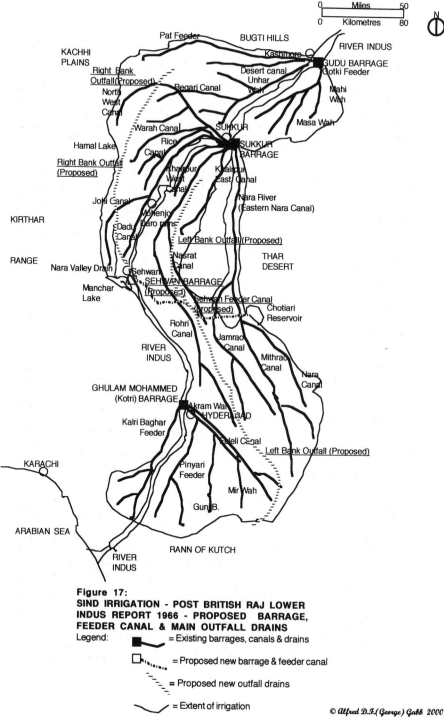

Figure 17:
SIND IRRIGATION - POST BRITISH RAJ LOWER INDUS REPORT 1966 - PROPOSED BARRAGE, FEEDER CANAL & MAIN OUTFALL DRAINS

Legend:

■▬ = Existing barrages, canals & drains

□▪▪▪▪ = Proposed new barrage & feeder canal

▟▟▟ = Proposed new outfall drains

⌒ = Extent of irrigation

© *Alfred D.F. (George) Gabb 2000*

Nawabshah, Sanghar and Mirpur Khas districts. Also irrigation and drainage tubewells on the right bank have been completed, and 56 of the 45 ton steel gates on the Sukkur Barrage replaced in 1984. The latter had financial assistance from the British Overseas Development Admistration (O.D.A.), now Department for International Development (D.F.I.D.). The 365 canal head regulator gates in the barrage system are also the subject of replacement, the Nara Canal is in the process of remodelling and the Chotiari Reservoir is being embanked.

R.T. Cobb and L.J.M. Coleby in the very graphic and fascinating Advanced Level Geography 'Monsoon Lands'[2] has, in addition to earlier scheme details above, given some very interesting maps showing the percentage of irrigated land, and the area and comparison of irrigation methods, on a provincial basis in the sub-continent. These indicated that in general the density of irrigated land in 1966 in the Sind was 100 percent, and in the Punjab from 60 to 80 percent. The Gangetic plain varied from 12 to 44 percent, Assam 25 percent, and the east coast of India from 22 to 25 percent. Maharashtra (Bombay), Mysore and Madhya Pradesh (C.P.) had only 5 to 6 percent. Whereas off-river canals are predominent in the Sind and Punjab, with a large percentage of wells in the latter, wells exceed canals in Uttar Pradesh (U.P.) and Maharashtra (Bombay), and by a considerable amount in the latter. In Tamil Nadu (Madras) and Andhra Pradesh (Hyderabad) off-river canals and tank (reservoir) irrigation are roughly equal.

During the construction of the British Raj irrigation canals, headworks and barrages the Consulting Engineers, Contractors and their men lived in temporary camps at strategic points where conditions were very harsh. On completion of construction permanent Canal Colonies were built, especially at the headworks where the headquarters was located, and well clear of the Indian city, to house the European, Anglo-Indian and senior Indian officers who maintained and ran the great irrigation systems. Offices and accomodation were also located within the region.

2. Mohenjo-Daro -

The ancient city of Mohenjo-Daro, circa 2,500 B.C., is located on the west bank of the River Indus, some 50 miles south west of Sukkur, and 250 miles from Karachi. One theory is that the Aryans, who were alleged to have invaded India in circa 1,500 B.C., were responsible for its destruction and with it, it's sister city of Harrapa, 100 miles south of Lahore in the Punjab, together with many smaller towns and villages of the same period, thus ending a highly sophisticated Indus Valley civilisation. The ruins of Mohenjo-Daro ('mound of the dead'), which extends to about a square mile, were discovered in 1922 when they were first excavated by the team of Sir John Marshall, then the English Director of the Indian Archaeological Service. Further digging followed under the direction of the eminent English archaeologist Sir Mortimer Wheeler, a later Director-General of Archaeology in India, who exposed the whole city. The city and the artifacts found, are comprehensively described in Sir Mortimer's book 'The Indus Civilisation.'[21]

The Indus civilisation is considered contemporary with the ancient civilisation of Mespotamia, arguably the oldest traced in the world after Egypt. The astonishing array of artifacts traced include bronze weapons, a steatite dancing girl, and wild and domesticated animals on steatite seals, including an elephant, and rhinoceros, in addition to bullocks, suggesting that this arid desert terrain must once have been wet, tropical jungle and savannah. There were also gold and steatite necklaces, terra cotta pots and figures of humans, animals, and also it is supposed figures of the Mother Goddess, and the god *Shiva*. There are also models of two-wheeled bullock carts similar in design to those still used in the Sind today, as squeaking solid axled wheels still give testimony to, as I was to experience at dead of night in Sukkur in 1965. All are lovingly preserved in an adjacent museum. Unfortunately the language of ancient Mohenjo-Daro, of which there is evidence in the artifacts, has tantalisingly not yet been deciphered, as it could tell us much of early irrigation and many other issues of the life of the inhabitants. It is hypothesised that the peoples of the Indus valley, depending on their level in society, worshipped *Shiva*, a fertility god, symbolised in worship by a *linga*, a Mother Goddess, and god Kings, before the arrival of the Aryans. The former two gods survived in the modern *Hindu* religion, but Hinduism is said to have developed further by embracing some of the religious philosophy of the Aryans. The ruins of Harappa were unfortunately wrecked in the 19th century, when the fired brick from which the ancient buildings were built, were plundered for rail ballast by the British contractors constructing the Lahore-Multan railway, and otherwise by local builders. Present day Mohenjo-Daro shows the remains of an elaborate and well engineered city, with brick buildings lining lanes and wide streets laid out on a grid pattern, with roadside drains, a large granary and even a substantial Roman-style bath.6,21

Although well cared for generally, the fired brick fabric of Mohenjo-Daro is steadily crumbling away, through the effect of waterlogging and salinity. This is an unfortunate and costly legacy left to Pakistan by the British, who never replaced the surrounding protective earth in the excavations, following documentation of the finds, as is common practice in modern time with at-risk structures. Ironically if they had, these significant Pakistani heritage sites would not have become one of the most important tourist attractions in the country. Up to the time that the British left India, only 15 years after the opening of the Sukkur Barrage in 1932, the whole barrage command had not been developed, and the groundwater table was fairly stable and at some depth, posing no dampness problem to the buildings. Since independence however the watertable had been steadily rising nearer to the surface, without any land drainage to cope with the waste water from *pancho* cultivation of rice and the otherwise excessive local irrigation. This failure to install land drainage in the region is another regrettable legacy of the British, (see above). The result was waterlogging of the foundations, causing rising dampness drawing up salinity. Furthermore, as opposed to the water application of surrounding irrigated fields, the city area receives only a little rain to wash the accumulation of salt into the ground and down to the watertable. It has in consequence ended up like a giant evaporation pan for the surrounding waterlogged fields, accumulating more and more salt in the soil. The rapid drying effect of the intense heat of the sun on the walls, causes the salt to crystallise at the brick surface resulting in exfoliation and crumbling. Basic preservation measures have been practised for many years, using mud packs on top of the walls, from which the rains wash down slurry over the wall faces, to provide a sacrificial skin against saline exfoliation. Unfortunately the northern Sind receives less than four inches of rain a year, which is hardly enough to even sustain this basic protection measure in an area where the evapo-transpiration reaches six feet annually. I carried out an investigation of the cause and effect of damage in 1962, for the Sir Murdoch MacDonald & Partners, Consulting Engineers. Later United Nations Educational, Scientific and Cultural Organisation (U.N.E.S.C.O.) and also Pennsylvania University of U.S.A. and others did also, with the aim to better preserve these historic ruins for posterity. Some work was started in 1962 by the Departments of Irrigation, Agriculture, Forestry and Archaeology, with the installation of two tubewells to draw down the watertable, the installation of additional surface catch water drains surrounding the area, and with test applications of sodium silicate, but shortage of funds interfered with progress.[5,6]

Aerial photograph of Mohenjo-Daro in 1965-
(With acknowledgements to Hunting Technical Services Ltd., Herts.)
Scale: 1/40,000

HINDUSTANI/ENGLISH GLOSSARY

acha - good;I understand; all right
amir - *Muslim* chief, or prince
    especially in the Sind
ashram - community
Anglo-Indian - person of mixed
    European and Indian blood
    where the original father was
    European
Angrezi - English, *European*
Angrezi log - English people
ayah - Indian nursemaid
badmash - bad people, criminals
bagh - garden
bapu - father
bazaar - market
begum - upper class *Muslim* lady,wife
bibighar - wife, or mistress' house
Billayati - (or *Blighty*); land across
    the seas; Europe, England
bungalow - single story house
burra sahib - big master
cantonment - British military
    station
chapaties - wheat pancake bread
chota sahib - small master
chowkidar - watchman, guard
chullao - come; go
dak bungalow- post rest house
dhal - lentils
dhobi - washerman
dhobi ghat - outdoor collective
    washing area
dustoorie - commission
eschul - school
fakir - holy man, saint
ferringhi - foreigner
ghats - mountains (as Western
    Ghats)
harem - collection of wives and
    concubines of one master
kala pani - black water, ocean,sea
khana - place: food
kharif - summer
kubi nai - not ever, never
kukri - *large Gurkha* knife
kutcha - raw, inferior, impermanent
maharajah - great, or major *Hindu*
    male ruler or king

maharani - great, or major *Hindu*
    female ruler, or queen;
    wife of *maharajah*
mahatma - great soul
mehtar - sweeper
memsahib - title of respect for a
    lady, usually a *European*
    lady during the British
    Raj
mofussil - countryside; outside the
    towns
monsoon - seasonal rainfall
nai - no
nautch - dance
nawab - *Muslim ruler*, or prince
nizam - hereditary title of the
    reigning prince of Hyderabad
paisa - money
pani - water
peshwa - chief minister
pukka - ripe, proper, permanent, real
rabi - winter
raj - rule
rajah - minor *Hindu* male ruler, or
    king
rani - minor *Hindu* female ruler, or
    queen; wife of *rajah*
ruhmal - square piece of cloth, a
    handkerchief
rupia - rupee(Indian money standard)
sahib - title of respect for a
    gentleman, usually a
    European, during the British
    Raj; master
Satyagraha (non-violent resistance
    or non-co-operation)
sepoy - Indian foot soldier
shikar - hunt; hunting
shikari - hunter
sirkar - government, rulers
sultan - major *Muslim* ruler
suttee - voluntary burning of *Hindu*
    widow on husband's funeral
    pyre
swaraj - home rule
thugee - ritual murder by strangling
    in the name of the *Hindu*
    god Kali
tulwar - curved sword
zamindar - landowner

SELECT BIBLIOGRAPHY
(Published in London, unless otherwise stated)

The Moving Finger writes; and having writ
Moves on: Nor all your Piety nor Wit
Shall lure it back to cancel half a Line,
Nor all your Tears wash out a Word of it.

(*The Rubàyàt of Omar Khayyam* 1070-1123)

PART 1 - Anglo-Indians

1. Abel, Evelyn - *The Anglo-Indian Community*, (Chanakya, Delhi 1988)
2. Anthony, Frank - *Britain's Betrayal in India; The Story of the Anglo-Indian Community*, (Allied Publishers, New Delhi 1969).
3. Allen, Charles (Ed) - *A Scrapbook of British India 1877 - 1947*, (Andrè Deutsch1977)
4. Anglo-Indian Review - *The Journal of the All India Anglo-Indian*, (Delhi)
5. Bayley, Victor - *Permanent Way Through the Khyber*, (Jarrolds 1939)
6. Bidwell, Shelford - *Sword for Hire: European Mercenaries in Eighteenth Century India*, (John Murray 1971)
7. Birkenhead, Lord - *Rudyard Kipling*, (Random House, New York 1978)
8. Bowling, A. H. - *British Hussar Regiments 1805-1914*, (Almark, Surrey 1972)
9. Bristow, Brigadier R.C.B. - *Memories of the British Raj - Soldier in India*, (Johnson1974)
10. British Government - *Government of India Act 1935*, (HMS 1935)
11. - *British Nationality Acts 1948, 1965, 1981, 1983*, (HMSO as stated)
12. - *Commonwealth Immigration Act 1962*, (HMSO, 1962)
13. Buckland, C.E. - *Dictionary of Indian Biography*, (Sonnenschein1906)
14. Clarke, W.G. - *Horse Gunners; The Royal Horse Artillery*, (Clarke1993)
15. Clarke, T.G. - *The Fortunes of the Anglo-Indian Race, considered retrospectively and prospectively: by one of fifty years knowledge and experience*, (Madras 1878)
16. Clay, John - *John Masters; A Regimental Life*, (Michael Joseph 1992)
17. Craig, Hazel Innes - *Under the Old School Topee*, (BACSA 1990 & Hazel Craig, Hertfordshire 1996)
18. Cross, Colin - *The Fall of the British Empire*, (Hodder & Stoughton 1968)
19. Dalrymple, William - *Brahminised Britons*, (Art. in 'The British Empire', Daily Telegraph 1997)
20. Daniel R.H. - *The Development of Anglo-Indian Education and its Problems*, (Unpublished thesis Univ. of Leeds, 1941)
21. Dewey, Clive - *Anglo-Indian Attitudes: The Mind of the Indian Civil Service*, (Hambledon 1994)
22. Dover, Cedric - *Cimmerri, or Eurasians in the Future*, (Modern Art Press, Calcutta 1929)
23. - *Half Caste*, (Secker & Warburg 1937)
24. - *Hell in the Sunshine; The Forgotten Children*, (Secker & Warburg 1943)
25. - *Henri Derozio, Eurasian Poet, Preceptorand Philosopher*, (Calcutta 1930)
26. Edwards, Thomas - *Henry Derizio, The Eurasian Poet, Teacher and Journalist*, (Calcutta 1884)
27. Edwardes, Michael - *British India*, (Sidgwick & Jackson, London 1967)
28. - *Glorious Sahibs*, (Eyre & Spottiswoode, 1968)
29. *Encyclopaedia Britannica*, (William Benton 1973)
30. Fox, Robin Lane - *Alexander the Great*, (Allen Lane 1973)
31. Gabb, Alfred D.F. (C.Eng.,MICE) - *Saving the Relics of Mohenjo-Daro*, (Art. Indus Journal, W.A.P.D.A., Lahore 1964)
32. Gaikwad V.R. - *The Anglo-Indians*, (Asia Pub. House, Bombay 1967)
33. Geo.International - *World Maps - India*, (Geo. International,Berlin 1995)
34. - 1. *North Western Region*
35. - 2. *North Eastern Region*
36. - 3. *Southern Region*
36. Gidney H. - *The Future of the Anglo-Indian Community*,

(Asiatic Review, Calcutta Jan. 1934)
37. Goodrich, Dorris - *The Making of an Ethnic Group: The Eurasian Community in India,*
    (Unpublished University of California, Berkley, USA 1952)
38. Grimshaw, Allen D. - *The Anglo-Indian Community:The Integration of a Marginal Group,*
    (Journal of Asian Studies, Feb.1959)
39. Hailsham, Lord, of St Marylebone (Ed.)-*Halsbury's Laws of England,*(Butterworth 1992)
40. Hankin, Nigel B. - *Hanklyn - Janklin,* (Banyan Books, New Delhi 1992)
41. Hannah, W.H. - *Bobs, Kipling's General,* (1972)
42. Hawes, Christopher J. - *Poor Relations,* (Curson Press 1996)
43. Heron, S.F. - *Anglo-Indians and Eurasians,* (1881)
44. Hennesy, Maurice - *The Rajah from Tipperary,* (New English Library, 1972)
45. Hindle - *A Survey of the Anglo-Indian Community,*
    (YMC Association Press, Calcutta 1924-1926)
46. Holland, Sir Henry - *Frontier Doctor, An Autobiography,* (Hodder & Stoughton 1958)
47. Holman, Dennis - *Sikander Sahib,* (Heinemann, 1961)
48. Ingels L. - *Anglo-Indian Amalgamation: The Pressing Need of the Community,*
    (Calcutta 1918)
49. James, Lawrence (Ed.) - *The British Empire, 1497 - 1997,* (Daily Telegraph 1997)
50. Johnson, Donald J., Johnson, Jean E., & Clark, Leon E. - *Through Indian Eyes,*
    (A CITE Book, New York 1992)
51. Kincaid, Dennis - *British Social Life in India 1608 - 1937,* (George Routledge 1938)
52. Luiz A.A.D. - *Anglo-Indians of Kerala,* (1960)
53. MacMunn, Lt. General Sir George - *The Armies of India,* (Crecy Books, Bristol 1971)
54. Magnussen, Magnus (Ed.) - *Chambers Biographical Dictionary*
    (Chambers, Edinburgh 1992)
55. Maher, Reginald - *These are the Anglo-Indians,* (Swallow Press,Calcutta 1962)
56. Masters, John- *Bhowani Junction,* (Michael Joseph 1954)
57.   - *Bugles and the Tiger,* (Michael Joseph 1956)
58.   - *The Road Past Mandalay,* (Harper & Michael Joseph,1961)
59. Milligan, Spike - *It Ends With Magic: A Milligan Family History,* (Penguin Books1990)
60. Mitra S.M. - *Anglo-Indian Studies,* (Longmans, Green 1913)
61. Moncrieff, Major-General Sir George Scott - *Canals & Campaigns,* (BACSA 1987)
62. Moore, Gloria Jean - *The Anglo Indian Vision,*(A. E. Press, Melbourne 1986)
63. Moorhouse, Geoffrey. - *India Britannica,* (Havill Press 1983)
64. Moreno, H.W.B. - *The Call to Arms for Anglo-Indians,* (Central Press, Calcutta 1916)
65.   - *Some Anglo-Indian Terms and Origins,*
    (Procs. of Indian Historical Commission Jan. 1923)
66. Muggeridge, Malcolm - *Something Beautiful for God: Mother Teresa of Calcutta,*
    (Collins 1971)
67. Naidis, Mark - *British Attitudes Towards the Anglo-Indians,*
    (South Atlantic Quarterly, Summer 1963)
68. Paul, F.X. - *Hundred Years of the Glorious Past: Story of St Joseph's College,*
    (St Joseph's E H School Annual, Bangalore 1968)
69. Payne, Withbert W. - *Anglo-Indian Education: Books & Articles,*
    (Withbert Payne, Walnut Creek, California 1995)
70. Pearse, Col. Hugh - *The Hearsays: Five Generations of an Anglo-Indian Family,*
    (William Black 1905)
71. Ray, Chaudri - *Henry Derozio, Eurasian Poet and Reformer,*
    (Metropolitan Book Agency, Calcutta 1966)
72. Reynolds H.G. - *The Anglo-Indian Manifesto,* (Lahore 1946)
73. Rhodes, J. - *Political India ,* (1932)
74. Robby, C.T. - *The Anglo-Indian Force,* (1916)
75. Roberts, Field Marshal Earl - *Forty One Years in India,* (Macmillan,1905)
76. Roy W.T. - *Hostages to Fortune,* (A Socio-Political Study of the Anglo-Indian Remnant in
    India), (Plural Societies, Summer 1974)
77. Sandes, Lt.Col. E.W.C. - *The Military Engineer in India,*
    (2 Vols.-The Institution of Royal Engineers, Chatham 1933 & 1935)
78. Saroop, Narindar - *A Squire of Hindustan,* (Nottingham Court Press,1983)
79. Scott, Paul - *Staying on,* (Book Club Associates:Heinemann, Bungay,Suffolk 1977)

80. Shakespear, Col.L.W. - *A Local History of Poona and its Battlefields*, (Macmillan 1916)
81. Snell, O. - *Anglo-Indians and Their Future*, (Thackers, Bombay 1944)
82. Staines, James Richard - *Country Born*, (Croscombe Press 1986)
83. Stark, Herbert Alick - *Hostages to India, or The Life Story of the Anglo-Indian Race*, (Fine Art College Calcutta 1926/1936)
84. - *John Ricketts and His Times*, (Wilson & Son, Calcutta 1934)
85. - *The Call of the Blood, or Anglo-Indians and the Sepoy Mutiny*, (British Burma Press, Rangoon 1932)
86. Stark, H.E. & Madge, Walter - *East Indian Worthies, Being Memoirs of Distinguished Indo-Europeans*, (Cambridge Steam Printing Works, Calcutta)
87. Taraporevala - *Up-to-Date Guide to Poona and Environment, with Maps*, (Taraporevala, Poona 1934)
88. Taylor, Neville C. - *Sources for Anglo-Indian Genealogy in the Library of the Society of Genealogists*, (Soc. of Genealogists 1990)
89. Turner, Steve - *Cliff Richard, The Biography*, (Lion 1993)
90. Twain, Mark - *The Adventures of Huckleberry Finn*, (1884)
91. Varma, Lal Bahadur - *Anglo-Indians*, (Reena Roy, New Delhi 1979)
92. Wallace, Kenneth E - *The Eurasian Problem Constructively Approached*, (Thackeray, Spink, Calcutta 1930)
93. - *Life of Sir Henry Gidney*, (A. Mukerjee,Calcutta 1945)
94. - *Brave New Anglo-India, in Brave New India, in Brave New World*, (Modern Art Press, Calcutta 1935)
95. Warden J.J. - *Problems of the Domiciled Community in Modern Light*, (Madras 1915)
96. Watson, Francis - *India, a Concise History*, (Thames & Hudson, New York 1979)
97. Webster, Mirriam - *Webster's Third New International Dictionary*, (Encyclopaedia Britannica, London 1966)
98. Weston C.N. - *Great Britain's Hostages to India, The Anglo-Indians, Their Magna Carta*, (Baldwins Boys High School, Bangalore 1955)
99. - *Anglo-Indian Revolutionaries of the Methodist Episcopal Church*, (Scripture Literature Press, Bangalore 1938)
100. Westwood, J.N. - *Railways of India*, (David & Charles, Newton Abbot, Devon 1974)
101. Wheeler, Sir Mortimer - *The Indus Civilisation*, (Cambridge University Press 1953)
102. Williams, L.F. Rushbrook - *Murrays Handbook for Travellers in India,Pakistan, Burma and Ceylon*, (John Murray,1962)
103. Wilson - *The Domiciled European and Anglo-Indian Race of India*, (Bombay 1926)
104. *Whitakers Almanac*, (1892 - 1946)
105. Yule, Col. Henry & Burnell A. C. - *Hobson Jobson*, (Rupa,Calcutta 1886

PART 2 - British-Indian History

1. Allen, Charles (Ed) - *A Scrapbook of British India 1877 - 1947*, (Andrè Deutsch 1977)
2. Allen, Louis - *Burma; The Longest War 1941-1945*, (Dent & Sons,1984)
3. Armitage, Sir Michael - *The Royal Air Force: An Illustrated History*, (Cassell, 1993)
4. Bartholemew, John - *Bartholemew's Map of India, Pakistan & Ceylon*, (John Bartholemew, Edinburgh 1963
5. Bidwell, Shelford - *Sword for Hire: European Mercenaries in Eighteenth Century India*, (John Murray1971)
6. Bosworth Smith, H. - *Life of Lord Lawrence*, (Thomas Nelson 1885)
7. Bowling, A.H. - *British Hussar Regiments 1805 - 1914*, (Almark, Surrey 1972)
8. Bristow, Brigadier R.C.B. - *Memories of the British Raj - Soldier in India*, (Johnson, 1974)
9. British Broadcasting Corporation - *Timewatch*, (BBC 2 TV, London, 8 October 1996)
10. British Broadcasting Corporation, *The Real Story of the Bridge over the River Kwai*, (Timewatch, BBC 2 TV London, 28 October 1997)
11. Buckland, C.E. - *Dictionary of Indian Biography*,(Sonnenschein 1906)
12. Churchill, Sir Winston Spencer - *The Story of the Malakhand Field Force*, (Longman, Green 1898)
13. - *A History of the English Speaking People*, (4vols,Cassell 1954 - 1958)
14. - *The Second World War*, (6 vols, Cassell 1948 - 1954)

ANGLO-INDIAN LEGACY   SELECT BIBLIOGRAPHY

15. Clarke, W.G. - *Horse Gunners; The Royal Horse Artillery*, (Clarke 1993)
16. Clay, John - *John Masters; A Regimental Life*, (Michael Joseph,1992)
17. Collins, Larry & Lapierre, Dominique - *Freedom at Midnight*, (Collins, 1975)
18. Commonwealth War Graves Commission - *The Burma - Siam Railway and its Cemeteries*, (CWGC Information Sheet, Maidenhead, Berks. 1997)
19. Craven, Rev. Thomas - *The New Royal Hindustani Dictionary*, (Methodist Publishing House, Lucknow 1932)
20. Cross, Colin - *The Fall of the British Empire*, (Hodder & Stoughton 1968)
21. Diver, Maud- *The Unsung, A Record of British Services in India*,(William Blackwood 1945)
22. Edwardes, Michael - *Glorious Sahibs*, (Eyre & Spottiswoode 1968)
23.   - *The Last Years of British India*, (Cassell 1963)
24.   - *British India*, (Sidgwick & Jackson 1967)
25. Elphick, Peter - *Singapore: The Pregnable Fortress*, (Hodder & Stoughton,1995)
26. *Encyclopaedia Britannica*, (William Benton 1973)
27.   - *Britannica Book of the Year* (Annually 1964-1986-William Benton)
28. Ennis, John - *Bombay Explosion*, (Cassell 1959)
29. Fergusson, Bernard - *Beyond the Chindwin*, (William Collins,1945)
30. Fox, Robin Lane - *Alexander the Great*, (Allen Lane, London 1973)
31. Gabb, Alfred D.F.(C.Eng.,MICE) - *Saving the Relics of Mohenjo-Daro*, (Indus Journal, W.A.P.D.A., Lahore 1964)
32. Gandhi, Mohandas Karimchand - *An Autobiography, or The Story of My Experiments with Truth*, (Penguin 1982)
33. Gardner, Brian - *The East India Company*, (Dorset Press, New York 1990)
34. Garratt, G.T. & Thompson E.J. - *The Rise and Fulfilment of British Rule in India*, (1934)
35. Geo. Centre International - *World Map 1:2,000,000-India* (Geo. Centre International, Berlin 1993/94)
                              - 1. *Southern Region*
36.   - 2. *North Eastern Region*
37.   - 3. *North Western Region*
38. Gilbert, Sir Martin - *Churchill; A Life*, (The Pocket Edition, Mandarin,1993)
39. Hamilton, Nigel - *Monty: The Making of a General*, (Hodder & Stoughton 1981)
40.   - *Monty: The Man behind the Legend*, (Lennard, Herts. 1987)
41. Hannah, W.H. - *Bobs, Kipling's General*, (1972)
42. Harfield, Alan - *The Indian Army of the Empress 1861 - 1903*, (Spellmount, Tunbridge Wells, Kent 1990)
43. H.M.S.O. - *Wings of the Phoenix: The Official Story of the Air War in Burma*, (Air Ministry, 1949)
44. Holman, Dennis - *Sikander Sahib*, (Heinemann 1961)
45. Jackson, Robert - *Thirty Seconds at Quetta: The Story of the Earthquake*, (Evans Bros.1960)
46. James, Lawrence (Ed.)- *The British Empire, 1497 - 1997*, (Daily Telegraph 1997)
47. James, Richard Rhodes - *Chindit*, (John Murray 1980)
48. Kipling, Rudyard - *A Choice of Kipling's Verse*,(T.S.Elliot Ed. - Faber & Faber 1941)
49. Kincaid, Dennis - *The Grand Rebel; An Impression of Shivaji, Founder of the Maratha Empire*, (Collins, London 1937)
50.   - *British Social Life in India 1608 - 1937*, (Routledge, London 1938)
51. Lewin, Ronald - *Slim - The Standard Bearer*, (Leo Cooper 1976)
52. MacMunn, Lt.General Sir George - *The Armies of India*,(Black,1911)
53. Magnussen, Magnus (Ed.) - *Chambers Biographical Dictionary* (Chambers, Edinburgh 1992)
54. Majumdar, Lt.Col. B.N. - *Short History of the Indian Army*, (Hendon, Nelson, Lancs 1971)
55. Masters, John - *Bugles and the Tiger*, (Michael Joseph 1956)
56.   - *The Road Past Mandalay*, (Michael Joseph,1961)
57. Mersey, Viscount - *The Viceroys and Governors- General of India 1757 - 1947* (John Murray 1949)
58. Moncrieff, Major-General Sir George Scott - *Canals & Campaigns*, (BACSA, 1987)
59. Moorhouse, Geoffrey. - *India Britannica*, (Havill Press, London 1983)
60. Mountbatten, Earl - *Mountbatten - Eighty Years in Pictures*, (Macmillan,1970)
61. Neillands, Robin - *A Fighting Retreat: The British Empire 1947 - 1997*,

137

(Hodder & Stoughton 1996
62. Palit, Major-General D.K. - *The Lightning Campaign - The Indo-Pakistan War 1971,*
(Thomson Press, New Delhi 1972)
63. Partington, Angela, *The Oxford Dictionary of Quotations,* (OUP 1998)
64. Probert, Air Commander Henry - *The Forgotten Airforce* (1996)
65. Roberts, Andrew - *Eminent Churchillians,* (1994)
66. Roberts, Field Marshall Earl - *Forty One Years in India,* (Macmillan, 1905)
67. Rolo, C. J. - *Wingate's Raiders,* (Harrap 1944)
68. Russell, Wing Commander W. W. - *Forgotten Skies,* (Hutchinson,1945)
69. Sandes, Lt.Col. E.W.C.- *The Military Engineer in India,*
(2 Vols.- Inst. of Royal Engineers, Chatham 1933/35)
70. Saroop, Narindar - *A Squire of Hindustan,* (Nottingham Court Press, 1983)
71. Shakespear, Col. L.W. - *Poona and its Battlefields,* (Macmillan,1916)
72. Slim, Field Marshal Sir William J- *Defeat into Victory,* (Cassell 1956)
73. Spear, Percival - *A History of India-* (Vol. 2, Penguin Books,1965)
74. Stark, Herbert Alick - *The Call of the Blood, or Anglo-Indians and the Sepoy Mutiny*
(British Burma Press,Rangoon 1932)
75.   - *India Under Company and Crown*
76. Sykes, Majorie - *An Indian Tapestry; Quaker Threads in the History of India, Pakistan &*
Bangladesh, from the Seventeenth Century to Independence,
(Sessions Book Trust, York 1997)
77. Swinterton, Col.I.S. - *The Army in India,* (The Midland Ancestor:Journal of Birmingham
& Midland Society for Genealogy & Heraldry Vol.10 No.2 Dec.1994)
78. Telegraph, Daily - *The British Empire 1497 - 1997,* (Daily Telegraph 1997)
79. TTK Maps -*Discover India Series-Road Guide to Maharashtra,*
(TTK Pharma, Madras 1995)
80. Ward, Andrew - *Our Bones are Scattered-The Cawnpore Massacres and the Indian Mutiny*
of 1857, (John Murray 1996)
81. Watson, Francis - *India, a Concise History,* (Thames & Hudson, New York 1979)
82. White, Sir Bruce - *The Artificial Invasion Harbour called MULBERRY -*
A Personal story by Sir Bruce White (1980)
83. Williams, L.F. Rushbrook - *Murrays Handbook for Travellers in India,Pakistan, Burma*
and Ceylon, (John Murray 1962)
84. Zeigler, Philip - *Mountbatten; the Official Biography,* (Guild Publishing,1985)

APPENDIX 1 -Governors-General & Viceroys of British India

1.   Mersey, Viscount - *The Viceroys and Governors - General of India 1757 - 1947*
(John Murray 1949)

APPENDIX 2 - Anglo-Indian Schools

1.   Abel, Evelyn - *The Anglo-Indian Community: Survival in India,*
(Chanakhia Publications, Delhi 1988)
2.   Anthony, Frank - *Britain's Betrayal in India; The Story of the Anglo-India Community,*
(New Delhi & New York 1969)
3.   Barnes School - *The Barnicle: Annual Magazine of Barnes School, Deolali-*
Golden Jubilee Edition, (Wagle Press, Bombay 1975)
4.   Barnes School - *The Barnicle: Annual Magazine of Barnes School, Deolali,*
(Wagle Press Bombay 1993-94)
5.   Chatterton, Bishop Eyre - *Our English Church Schools in India,* (SPCK Pamphlet 1934)
6.   Coles, W.R. - *Forty Years On - Barnes School in Retrospect,* (Unpublished Art, Nasik 1969
)
7.   Craig, Hazel Innes - *Under the Old School Topee,* (BACSA 1990/Hazel Craig, Herts 1996)
8.   Council for the Indian School Certificate Examinations- *School List -*
(Govt. of India, New Delhi 1993)
9.   Daniel, H - *The Development of Anglo-Indian Education and its Problems,*
(Unpublished thesis Univ. of Leeds, 1941)
10. D'Souza, Austin - *Anglo-Indian Education: A Study of its Origins and Growth in Bengal up*

to 1860, (OUP, Delhi 1976)
11. *Encyclopaedia Britannica,* (William Benton 1973)
12. Gabb, Alfred D.F. (George) - *Barnes High School, Deolali -50 Years Ago and Now* (Unpub. Art., York 1997)
13.   - *St Joseph's College, Bangalore-60 Years Ago and Now,* (Unpub.Art., York 1997)
14. Gaikwad V.R. - *The Anglo-Indians,* (Asia Publishing House, Bombay 1967)
15. Hawes, Christopher J.- *Poor Relations; The Making of the Eurasion Community in British India 1773 - 1833,* (Curson, Surrey 1996)
16. Hopkirk, Peter - *Quest for Kim: In Search of Kipling's Great Game,* (John Murray 1996)
17. *Josephites Journal, The U.K. Summer 1994* - (Ed. Denis Whitworth, Croydon1994)
18. Kaul, H. K. (Ed.) - *Traveller's India: An Anthology,* (OUP 1979)
19. La Martinière College - *Constantia; Chronicle of La Martinière College, Lucknow,* (LMC, Lucknow, 1917. Pub. Annually)
20. Mitra, Chandan - *Constant Glory; La Martinière Saga 1836 - 1986,* (OUP, Bombay 1987)
21. Moore, Gloria Jean - *The Anglo-Indian Vision,* (A. E. Press, Melbourne 1986)
22. Moorhouse, Geoffrey - *India Britannica,* (Havill Press 1983)
23. Norris, Paul Byron - *Follow my Bangalory Man,* (BACSA 1996)
24. OBA - *OBA Calling - Magazine of the St Joseph's Boys High School, Bangalore Old Boys Association,* (S.J.B.H.S., Bangalore 1995-96. Pub Annually)
25. Paul, F. X. - *Hundred Years of the Glorious Past - The History of St Joseph's College,* (St Joseph's E.H.School Annual, Bangalore 1958)
26. Penny, Frank - *The Church in Madras,* (Smith Elder, 1900)
27. Roderick, Reginald - Echoes of Christchurch-Christ Church Boys & Girls School, Jubblupore, (Pte. Pub. 1997)
28. Stark, Herbert Alick - *Hostages to India, or The Life Story of the Anglo- Indian Race,* (Star Printing Works, Calcutta 1926/1936:BACSA Reprint 1987)
29.   - *John Ricketts and his Times,* (Wilsone,Calcutta 1934)
30. St Joseph's Boys' High School - *Annual Magazine of St Joseph's Boys'High School, Bangalore,*(S.J.B.H.S. , Bangalore 1993-94)
31. Stracey E. - *St Joseph's European High School, Bangalore* (St Joseph's College, Bangalore/Pte. pub. art. East Indies Telegraph No.3. 1991)
32. Taraporevala - *Taraporevala's Up-to-Date Guide to Poona and Environment,* (Taraporevala, Poona 1934)
33. Thomas, Cary (Ed.) - *The U.K. Josephites Journal-Summer 1999,* (St Joseph's Old Boys Association, U.K.)
34. Tyndale-Biscoe, E. D. - *Fifty Years Against the Stream: The Story of a School in Kashmir 1880 -1930,* (Wesleyan Mission Press, Mysore 1930)
35. Weston, C.N. - *The Story of Sixty Years; Baldwin High School, Bangalore 1880 - 1940,* (B.H.S., Bangalore 1940)
36.   - *Retrospect & Prospect, Baldwin High School, Bangalore 1880 - 1947* (B.H.S., Bangalore 1947)

APPENDIX 3 - Railways of British India

1. Aitken, Bill - *Exploring Indian Railways,* (OUP,Delhi 1994)
2. Bayley, Victor - *Permanent Way Through the Khyber,* (Jarrolds 1939)
3. Berridge, P.S.A. - *Couplings to the Khyber. The Story of the NorthWestern Railway,* (Augustus M Kelly, New York 1969)
4. Burton, Anthony - *The Railway Empire,* (John Murray 1994)
5. Davidson, Captain Edward- *The Railways of India,* (E & F N Spon,1868)
6. Diver, Maud - *The Unsung, A Record of British Services in India,*(William Blackwood 1945)
7. Gaikwad V.R. - *The Anglo-Indians,* (Asia Pub., Bombay 1967)
8. Indian Railways - *Trains at a Glance,* (Indian Railways Board, Bombay 1995)
9. Kerr, Ian J. - *Building the Railways of the Raj 1850-1900,* (OUP, Delhi 1995)
10. Kipling, Rudyard - *Rudyard Kipling's Verse,* Inclusive Edition 1885 - 1926, (Doubleday & Doran New York 1929)
11. Moncrieff, Major Gen. Sir George Scott - *Canals & Campaigns, An Engineer Officer in India 1877 - 1885,* (BACSA, 1987)

12. Sandes, Lt.Col.E.W.C.-*The Military Engineer in India*, (2 Vols.-The Inst. of Royal Engineers, Chatham 1933/35)
13. Satow, Michael & Ray, Desmond - *Railways of the Raj*, (Scolar Press, 1980)
14. Theroux, Paul - *By Rail Across the Indian Sub-continent*, (National Geographic Magazine. Vol.165 No.6, London June 1984)
15. Tully, Mark - *Famous Train Journeys*, (BBC TV, London 1994)
16. Westwood, J.N. - *Railways of India*, (David & Charles, Newton Abbot, Devon 1974)
17. Williams, L.F. Rushbrook - *Murrays Handbook for Travellers in India, Pakistan, Burma and Ceylon*, (John Murray,1962)

APPENDIX 4 - Irrigation in British India

1. Bosworth Smith, H. - *Life of Lord Lawrence*, (Thomas Nelson 1885)
2. Cobb, R.T. & Coleby, L.J.M. - *Monsoon Lands -Part 1 - General Introduction India, Pakistan, Ceylon & Burma*, (Advanced Level Geography, Book 6, University Tutorial Press,1966)
3. Diver, Maud - *The Unsung, A Record of British Services in India*,(William Blackwood 1945)
4. Edwardes, Michael - *British India*, (Sidgwick & Jackson, 1967)
5. Gabb, Alfred D.F. (C.Eng.,M.I.C.E.) - *Mohenj-daro: Interim Report on Investigations of Deterioration of Brickwork through Dampness and Salinity*, (Sir M.MacDonald & Partners, for W.A.P.D.A.,Unpublished, Hyderabad 1962)
6.   - *Saving the Relics of Mohenjo-Daro*, (Indus Journal, W.A.P.D.A.,Lahore 1964)
7. Gabb, Alfred D.F.(C.Eng.,MICE) et al- *Lower Indus Report - Present Situation - Water Use- Vol. 8*, (Hunting Technical Services & Sir Murdoch MacDonald & Ptrs, for W.A.P.D.A., Pte.Pub., Lahore 1966)
8. Gov't of India - *The Opening of The Lloyd Barrage and Canals by His Excellency The Earl of Willingdon, Viceroy and Governor General of India on Wednesday the 13th January 1932*,(Govt. Central Press, Bombay 1932)
9. Isrealson, Orson W. - *Irrigation Principles and Practices*, (John Wiley 1962)
10. Lambrick H.T. - *Sind, A General Introduction*, History of Sind Series Vol. 1, (Sindhi Adabi Board, Hyderabad),1964)
11. Moncrieff, Major-General Sir George Scott - *Canals & Campaigns*, (BACSA 1987)
12. Public Works Department - *Completion Report of the Lloyd Barrage and Canals Construction Scheme, Sind (1923 -33)*. Vols. III, IV, V, & VI, (Government of Bombay PWD, Bombay 1934)
13. Public Works Department - *Triennial Review of Irrigation in India,1918 - 1921*, (Govt. of India , Pte. Pub. Delhi 1921)
14. Sandes, Lt.Col. E.W.C.Sandes- *The Military Engineer in India*, (2 Vols.-Inst.of Royal Engineers, Chatham 1933 &1935)
15. Sharma K.R.- *Irrigation Engineering*, (Vols. 1&2, India Printers, Jullundur, India 1959)
16. Stone, Dr. Ian - *Canal Irrigation in British India*, (Cambridge University Press, London 1984)
17. Taraporevala - *Taraporevala's Up-to-Date Guide to Poona and Environment*, (Tarporevala, Poona 1934)
18. Water & Power Development Authority(W.A.P.D.A.) - *Development of the Lower Indus Region- A Summary of the Lower Indus Report*, (Prepared by Hunting Technical Services Ltd & Sir M. MacDonald & Ptrs, for W.A.P.D.A. Pte. Pub. Lahore 1966)
19.   - *Gudu Barrage Inauguration 1st March 1963*, (W.A.P.D.A. Printing Press, Lahore 1963)
20. Welch, John - *The Kaiser-I-Hind Medal*, (British Ancestors in India Society (B.A.I.S.), The Indiaman, (Art), Vol. 2,No.4 December 1997 ,Sheffield)
21. Wheeler, Sir Mortimer - *The Indus Civilisation*, (Cambridge University Press, Cambridge 1953)
22. Williams, L.F. Rushbrook - *Murrays Handbook for Travellers in India, Pakistan, Burma and Ceylon*, (John Murray, London 1962)